CATALOGUE

OF

INDIAN COINS

IN

THE BRITISH MUSEUM.

GREEK AND SCYTHIC KINGS OF BACTRIA
AND INDIA.

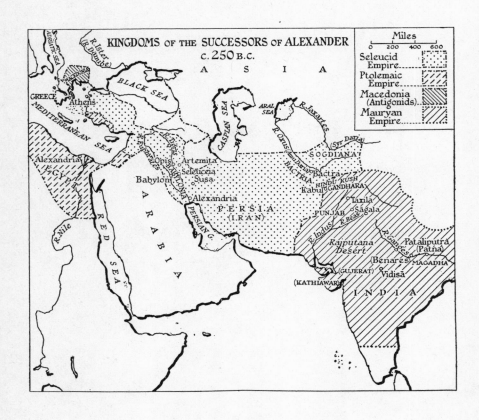

KINGDOMS OF THE SUCCESSORS OF ALEXANDER c. 250 B.C.

Miles
0   200   400   600

Seleucid Empire........
Ptolemaic Empire........
Macedonia (Antigonids)........
Mauryan Empire........

A   S   I   A

ADRIATIC SEA

R. Ister (R. Danube)

BLACK SEA

GREECE

Athens

MEDITERRANEAN SEA

MACEDONIA

CASPIAN SEA

ARAL SEA

R. Jaxartes

R. Oxus (Amu Daria)

R. Jaxartes (Syr Daria)

SOGDIANA

BACTRIA

Bactra

HINDU KUSH

Kabul

GANDHARA

Taxila

Ságala

PUNJAB

R. Beas

R. Indus

R. Ganges

Pataliputra (Patna)

Benares

MAGADHA

Vidiśā

Rajputana Desert

(GUJERAT)

(KATHIAWAR)

I   N   D   I   A

Alexandria

EGYPT

R. Nile

RED SEA

ARABIA

PERSIAN G.

Opis

Artemita

Seleuceia

Babylon

Susa

BABYLONIA

Alexandria

PERSIA (IRAN)

R. Tigris

R. Euphrates

THE COINS

OF THE

GREEK AND SCYTHIC KINGS

OF

BACTRIA AND INDIA.

IN

THE BRITISH MUSEUM.

Dept. of Coins and Medals

BY PERCY GARDNER, LITT. D.

DISNEY PROFESSOR OF ARCHAEOLOGY IN THE UNIVERSITY OF CAMBRIDGE.

EDITED BY

REGINALD STUART POOLE, LL.D.

CORRESPONDENT OF THE INSTITUTE OF FRANCE.

ARGONAUT, INC., PUBLISHERS

CHICAGO   MCMLXVI

Library of Congress Card Catalog Number: 66-25813

Printed in the United States of America

PREFACE TO THE FIRST AMERICAN EDITION

The extreme value of ancient coins as historical documents of primary importance is nowhere more important in the area of ancient Greek coinage than in the case of the Greek and Scythic kings of Bactria and India. Were it not for the inscribed coins and the relationship of types found in hoards, the history of this easternmost Hellenistic Empire would have been lost forever.

The special value of the present book lies primarily in the fact that as all great historians and numismatists concerned with this area admit, it is the best and most complete *corpus* of nearly all the known coin types issued by the hellenistic and hellenized kings and rulers of Bactria and India. Its reference value has not diminished in the eighty years since its first edition and it is still the primary source for cataloging and identifying the Greek and Scythic coins of India throughout the world in museums and commercial numismatic establishments.

Today, the historian who studies the great works on the Greeks in India by W. W. Tarn and A. K. Narain will feel the need undoubtedly to refer to the coins which these authors used as their main source materials. But before the issuance of the present reprint the book was so scarce as to be virtually unobtainable. The small number of copies of the original edition of 1886 were quickly absorbed by libraries and private collectors and even in the early years of the century the volume was considered to be 'scarce.' Therefore, it goes without saying that the possibility of a copy of this work existing in the newer libraries or in the seminars in ancient history of the shining glass and aluminum colleges of today is extremely remote.

So it is with pride and the feeling of performing a useful service for numismatists and historians that we release this reissue in the series *The Argonaut Library of Antiquities*.

It was considered necessary to offer readers of this edition the following new features: a map, a short bibliographical note and a chart of the relationships and dating of the Greek kings of Bactria and India showing the conclusions which have been reached to date. For the latter purpose the chart selected is the work of A. K. Narain as it offers the most advanced research on the subject thus far. In some cases it will be almost impossible for the non-specialist to ascertain whether the information therein is properly justified, but as Nahrain's own note points out, all dates are approximate and many are hypothetical. Those who care to may take further pains to confirm or deny them by seeking out excavation reports and articles in various journals, but for the most part, Nahrain's deductions seem to be as accurate as possible at our present level of knowledge.

A map showing the kingdoms of Alexander's successors immediately before the revolt against Seleucid rule, which resulted in two centuries of independence for the Greco-Bactrian kingdoms, has been used as the frontispiece. For more detailed maps and diagrams showing the easternmost Hellenistic Empire in various periods, the reader may consult the works of W.W. Tarn and A. K. Narain included in the bibliographical note.

AL. N. OIKONOMIDES
Editor, Argonaut Library of Antiquities

CHICAGO, JUNE 1966

CONTENTS.

*a**

BIBLIOGRAPHICAL NOTE

The basic references for the study of the history of the Greeks in Bactria and India are relatively few in number and an adequate reference library can be formed with the following books.

Narain, A. K. *The Indo-Greeks.* Oxford 1957. (With a select bibliography, pp. 182-190, which includes virtually everything of value on the subject and is especially strong in historical and numismatic literature).

Rapson, E. J., ed. *The Cambridge History of India,* vol. I (1922). Consult *ch.* 17 by Sir George Macdonald; *chs.* 18-20 by F. W. Thomas; *chs.* 21-23 by E. J. Rapson.

Smith, V. A. *Early History of India.* 4th ed. Oxford 1924.

Tarn, W. W. *The Greeks in Bactria and India.* 2nd ed. Cambridge 1951.

Trever, K. B. *Pamyatniki Greko-Baktriyskogo Iskusstva.* Moscow & Leningrad 1940.

Woodcock, G. *The Greeks in India* (in preparation).

NUMISMATIC REFERENCE

Clain-Stefanelli, E. *Select Numismatic Bibliography.* New York 1965.

Narain, A. K. *The Coin Types of the Indo-Greek Kings.* NNM, No. 1 of the Numismatic Society of India. 1957.

Simonetta, A. M. "A New Essay on the Indo-Greeks, the Sakas and the Pahlavas," in *East and West* 9, 1958, pp. 154 ff.

————. "Indo-Greci e Indo-Parthi, Sovrani: Numismatica artistica," in *Enciclopedia dell' Arte Antica,* vol. VI (1961), p.p. 153-157.

Smith, V. A. *A Catalogue of the Coins in the Indian Museum, Calcutta, including the Cabinet of the Asiatic Society of Bengal,* vol. I. Oxford 1906.

Whitehead, R. B. *Catalogue of Coins in the Punjab Museum, Lahore,* vol. I. *Indo-Greek Coins.* Oxford 1914.

————. "Commentary on Rare and Unique Coins," in Marshall's *Taxila.* vol. II. (1951), pp. 830-842.

Note: For further numismatic bibliography, again consult Narain's *The Indo-Greeks* which includes numerous entries of even the most remote periodical articles, etc.

EDITOR'S PREFACE.

———•••———

THE present volume contains all the coins which were issued by the Greek and Scythic kings who ruled in India and the neighbouring lands between the time of Alexander the Great and the third century A.D.

The work has been long and laborious, alike to compiler, editor, and printer. The number of unusual characters which it contains has greatly hindered its progress; but the typographical difficulties have not been the only ones. The history of the kings is very obscure, and the types employed on their coins often of a mixed and uncertain character. On the other hand, few fields of numismatics offer richer material, historical, archaeological, and even philological; though philological theories are necessarily excluded from these pages.

Special thanks are due to General Cunningham, R.E., who has allowed the compiler free use of his plates published in recent volumes of the Numismatic Chronicle, and has thus enabled the present work to be rendered far more complete than it could otherwise be: also to Professor Cecil Bendall, who has given valuable philological aid.

The system of transliteration adopted for Prakrit words is that used by Professor Aufrecht in the Sanskritic Catalogue of the Bodleian Library; also in the Catalogue of Books in the British Museum.

I have carefully revised the manuscript of this work, comparing each coin with the corresponding description.

REGINALD STUART POOLE.

THE COINS

OF THE

GREEK AND SCYTHIC KINGS

OF

BACTRIA AND INDIA.

A CHART SHOWING THE INDO-GREEK KINGS IN GENEALOGICAL AND CHRONOLOGICAL ARRANGEMENT

N.B. *The relationships and dates given below are based on the conclusions reached in this work. All dates are approximate and many are hypothetical.*

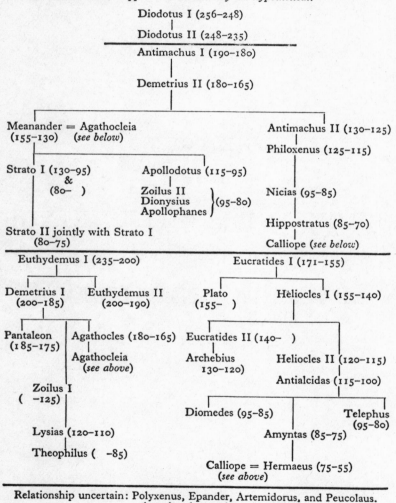

Diodotus I (256–248)

Diodotus II (248–235)

Antimachus I (190–180)

Demetrius II (180–165)

Meanander = Agathocleia   Antimachus II (130–125)
(155–130)   (see below)

Philoxenus (125–115)

Strato I (130–95)   Apollodotus (115–95)
     &
  (80–)   Zoilus II
                   Dionysius   } (95–80)   Nicias (95–85)
                   Apollophanes

Strato II jointly with Strato I   Hippostratus (85–70)
     (80–75)

Calliope (see below)

Euthydemus I (235–200)   Eucratides I (171–155)

Demetrius I   Euthydemus II   Plato   Heliocles I (155–140)
(200–185)   (200–190)   (155–)

Pantaleon   Agathocles (180–165)   Eucratides II (140–)   Heliocles II (120–115)
(185–175)
               Agathocleia   Archebius
               (see above)   130–120)

Antialcidas (115–100)

Zoilus I
(–125)

Diomedes (95–85)   Telephus
                                         (95–80)

Lysias (120–110)   Amyntas (85–75)

Theophilus (–85)

Calliope = Hermaeus (75–55)
(see above)

Relationship uncertain: Polyxenus, Epander, Artemidorus, and Peucolaus.
          (–130)   (–130)   (–95)   (–95)

Narain, A. K. *The Indo-Greeks.* Oxford 1957.

INTRODUCTION.

Necessity for here examining historical data. In treating of the arrangement of the coins of the Greek and Scythic Kings of Bactria and India, it is necessary to enter briefly into all the known facts of their history. The Kings of the Seleucid and Ptolemaic dynasties succeeded one another in a known order, and the chief events of their reigns have been handed down to us by ancient writers. It was therefore unnecessary to give the facts of their history as an introduction to the lists of the coins issued by them. But in regard to all but two or three of the kings of the farther East, the ancient historians are quite silent; and coins and inscriptions alone save us from ignorance even of their names. Therefore it is necessary in this Introduction to trace the outlines of any history which can now be recovered, and in particular in some detail to set forth the historical facts which may fairly be established by means of the coins. In order to bring the discussion into the narrowest possible limits, it will be necessary (1) to abstain from mere conjecture, however tempting; (2) to avoid full discussion of disputed points, merely indicating where difference of opinion exists, and referring, when possible, to works already published, or monographs in various numismatic journals; (3) to treat in detail only such parts of history as have a numismatic bearing.

The writers to whom credit is due for the arrangement and decipherment of these coins are, in the first rank, James Prinsep* and General Alexander Cunningham.†

---

* *Essays on Indian Antiquities.*
† Coins of the Successors of Alexander, *Numismatic Chronicle*, 1868, &c.

Mr. E. Thomas,* Lassen,† and Wilson,‡ have also done much important work, both historical and numismatic, in the same field. The most recent monograph on the coins is that of von Sallet,§ whose scholarly acquirements and solid numismatic judgment have enabled him to correct on many points the theories of his predecessors. Mr. James Fergusson's and Professor Cowell's researches have also been of the greatest value to the present purpose; and there is much valuable matter in von Gutschmid's article on the Graeco-Parthian Empire in the ninth edition of the *Encyclopædia Britannica*, s. v. *Persia*. When a debt is due to other writers, it will be mentioned in the foot-notes.

I. HISTORICAL OUTLINES.

The numismatics of the Greek rulers of India properly begins with Diodotus. But there are a few coins issued in India or neighbouring countries at an earlier period than his, which are, for convenience, included in this volume. Whether Alexander himself, during his sojourn in India, issued coins in his own name, may perhaps be doubted; but it is at least a plausible conjecture that certain bronze coins,‖ bearing the usual types of Alexander and his name, but of square form, were issued in India, as the custom of issuing square coins already existed in India in Alexander's time, but in no other country. These pieces, then, unfortunately wanting in the British Museum, may be considered as the earliest Greek coins of India.

Alexander the Great: Rulers who issued coin B.C. 330—260.

* Notes to Prinsep's *Essays*.
† *Indische Alterthumskunde*.
‡ *Ariana Antiqua*.
§ *Zeitschrift für Numismatik*, Berlin 1879.
‖ The conjecture is Dannenberg's, *Zeitschr. f. Num.* vi. 166 (note), who, however, gives the coins to Bactria. India is a far more reasonable attribution.

In recent years the region of Balkh (Bactria) has furnished an abundant supply of coins, issued by the immediate successors of Alexander in that district.* Among these are double darics, with Greek letters on the obverse; gold and silver coins of the first three Antiochi, with the types of a seated Apollo and of a horse's head; silver coins of Seleucus I., with types of a chariot of elephants and a horse's head; coins issued during the joint reigns of Seleucus and Antiochus I., bearing the names of both rulers; and gold money of an early king of the Persepolitan class, with Pehlvi legend.

Among these also have come to light a few coins, in gold and silver, of a king named Andragoras, who is con-

Andragoras.

jectured to have been ruler of Parthia or one of the neighbouring countries in the early part of the third century B.C. The only ancient authority who mentions this king is Justin,† who states Andragoras to have been the name of (1) a Persian noble set up as Satrap of Parthia by Alexander, (2) a Satrap of Parthia overthrown eighty years later by the first Arsaces. It is more probable that the coins published in our catalogue belong to the period of the second of these rulers. The issue of gold coin shows that the ruler who issued them claimed a complete independence; and this is a further reason for assigning him to the time of the break up of the Seleucid empire in the East, about B.C. 250.

The coins of Sophytes were first published by Cunningham.‡

Sophytes.

They are the more interesting because their date and place of issue can be approximately fixed. We learn from several of the historians of Alexander's reign that Sopeithes, or Sophytes, ruled a district on the banks of the Acesines

---

* P. Gardner, in *Num. Chron.* 1879, p. 1; 1880, p. 181; 1881, p. 8. Cunningham, in *R. A. S. B. Journal*, 1881, p. 151. Especially has a find from the Oxus river enriched the cabinets of collectors.

† Justin, xii. 4, xli. 4. Cf. *Num. Chron.* 1879, p. 1; 1881, p. 8.

‡ *Num. Chron.* 1866, p. 220.

at the time of Alexander's invasion, and was confirmed by the
latter in the possession of it. But Sophytes' coins are copied from
the issues, not of Alexander, but of Seleucus. It would appear
from them that Sophytes renewed with Seleucus, very probably on
the occasion of that king's eastern expedition against Sandracottus,
the friendship which he had established with Alexander.

After this expedition, for the period of a century, that is to say
during the third century before our era, India proper was governed
altogether by native rulers; the power of the Seleucidae and Greek
kings of Bactria stopping at the Indian Caucasus.

The date of the revolt of Bactria against the authority of the

The Bactrian
revolt.
Diodotus.

Seleucidae, who had inherited all the eastern parts
of the empire of Alexander, cannot be accurately
fixed. Justin,* however, states that it was contemporary with another revolt of one of the eastern provinces of
the Seleucid empire, that of the Parthians under Arsaces; an event
which took place in B.C. 248.† About that time, then, Diodotus,
Satrap of Bactria, revolted against Antiochus II. of Syria, and
succeeded in establishing his independence. He seems to have pre-
pared his subjects for a change of masters by issuing coin bearing the types of Antiochus II. of Syria, but with his own portrait.‡
After his establishment in the kingdom he continued this issue
unchanged, only substituting his own name, besides his portrait,
for that of the Seleucid king. According to Justin,§ Diodotus soon
died, and was succeeded by his son, also named Diodotus, who made
a treaty of alliance with Arsaces, the first Parthian king. But it
seems clear that all coins which have come down to us bearing the

---

* xli. 4.
† Gardner, *The Parthian Coinage*, p. 3.
‡ *Br. Mus. Catalogue of Seleucid Coins*, p. 15. Cf. *Num. Chron.* 1881, p. 11.
§ xli. 4. Justin calls Diodotus Theodotus. But Trogus Pompeius seems to
have had the name right, *Prol.* lib. xli.

name of Diodotus were issued by one king. We must therefore either suppose that Justin is wrong and has duplicated a single monarch, or that the younger Diodotus continued the issue of his father's money unchanged, or, finally, that the elder Diodotus continued during his lifetime to issue money in the name of Antiochus of Syria, and that our coins with the name of Diodotus were issued by his son, who first ventured to introduce his own name and portrait on the coin. Between these alternatives we cannot venture to decide; in favour of the last, it may be observed that the portrait of Diodotus on his coins is that of a man of not more than middle age; the coins of flat fabric, and bearing an elderly portrait, being now considered forgeries.

We learn that Diodotus was superseded in the rule of Bactria by Euthydemus, a native of Magnesia, in Ionia, possibly a Satrap of some neighbouring province, who was in full power at the time when Antiochus the Great made his eastern expedition, in or about B.C. 208. The accurate pages of Polybius* give us a glimpse into his history which is very valuable. Euthydemus being defeated in battle by Antiochus, and unable to oppose him, appealed to his generosity, saying that he was born in Asia Minor, and was not one of those who had revolted against Antiochus II., but, on the contrary, had gained the kingdom after rooting out the descendants of those who had so revolted. He pointed out the grave danger that must arise if he were obliged to call in the aid of the Scythians, who were already hovering on the Chinese frontier of his dominions. Antiochus seems to have been open to conviction: finally, he agreed to acknowledge Euthydemus' independence; and, taking a fancy to Demetrius his son, promised him one of his own daughters in marriage.

Euthydemus.
Eastern expedition of
Antiochus III.

* *Hist.* x. *ad fin.*, xi. 34.

After making terms with Euthydemus, Antiochus advanced across the Paropamisus into India, and made a treaty with the Indian king, Sophagasenus, or Subhāgasena, who seems at that time to have been in full possession of the Kabul Valley, the Greek dominion stretching little, if at all, to the south of the Indian Caucasus. Thence Antiochus returned, through Arachosia and Drangiana, to Syria.

With the beginning of the second century B.C. we find great changes taking place in the Greek regions of Central Asia. On the death of Euthydemus, his son Demetrius succeeded; and we find, as contemporary and rival of the latter, the great Eucratides, whose career of chequered victory and defeat may be partly traced in historical records. At the same time the Greeks, perhaps in consequence of the constantly increasing pressure from the north of the nomadic tribes of Central Asia, made their way across the Indian Caucasus, and began to wrest from the native Indian princes the districts of Kabul and the Panjab, which had been left under native dominion by the Seleucid kings from Seleucus I. to Antiochus III., and which Diodotus does not seem to have attacked; for coins of Diodotus are not found south of the Indian Caucasus. On the other hand, those of Euthydemus are found as far south as Seistan, and as far east as the Panjab;* and the city of Sagala, in the neighbourhood of Lahore, bore the surname of Euthydemia. Thus the sudden extension of the Greek pale would seem to have been a feature of the later years of Euthydemus. But it appears, from the statements of ancient writers, that the actual conqueror was not Euthydemus but his son Demetrius, who was probably his colleague in the kingdom as well as his successor. Thus Justin† speaks of

Side note: Demetrius and Eucratides: conquests to East & South

---

* Some were found in the Indus at Attok. See Cunningham, in *Num. Chron.*, 1869, p. 137.

† xli. 6.

Demetrius as king of India, and Strabo* couples him with Menander as a chief agent of Greek conquest in India. What seems most likely is that Demetrius made considerable conquests during his father's lifetime.

We are, however, scarcely justified in saying, as does v.Gutschmid,† that "Demetrius himself marched down the course of the Indus, conquered Pattala and the kingdom of Saraostes (Surāshtra) and Sigerdis, probably the district of the commercial city Barygaza." The careless language of the passage of Strabo in which these places are mentioned as within the Greek pale seems only to imply that some of the Greek kings extended their conquests so far; and it is reasonable to suppose that the rule of Menander was extended farther to south and east than that of Demetrius; to Menander therefore the conquest of the Indus valley may be with more reason ascribed.

Not only did Euthydemus acquire, through his son's activity, territory in India, but he also probably ruled the widest district ever possessed by the Greeks to the north of the Paropamisus, from Margiana to Chinese Tartary. Even into the Celestial Empire the influence and the trade of the Greeks seems at this time to have penetrated. Of this a proof is furnished by a coin brought by Sir D. Forsyth from Kashgar,‡ bearing a Chinese legend and inscribed with the name and titles of a Greek king, possibly Hermaeus. After Euthydemus' death his dominions were broken up by the rivalry between Demetrius and Eucratides, as well as by the rise and usurpations of fresh kings of uncertain origin, such as the first Antimachus.

---

* _Geog._ xl. 11, 1. Most of Strabo's statements as to early Bactrian history are loose and incorrect. For instance, he speaks of the revolt of Arsaces as subsequent to the rise of Euthydemus.

† In _Encycl. Brit._, Persia, p. 590.

‡ _Numism. Chron._ 1879, p. 274. That this coin is of iron, is now, I am informed, denied.

Of Eucratides also the origin is obscure. We know, however, by a
fortunate chance, the names of his father and mother.

Coins of Eucratides with his father and mother.
These are furnished to us by the remarkable coins *
which bear on one side the head of Eucratides, and
the inscription Βασιλεὺς Εὐκρατίδης; on the other
the portraits of his father and mother, Heliocles and Laodice. The
very collocation of the inscriptions which appear on the two sides
of those coins, Βασιλεὺς Εὐκρατίδης — ʽΗλιοκλέους καὶ Λαοδίκης,
where we seem almost compelled to understand the word υἱός,
shows that in them Eucratides intends to proclaim his parentage.
Heliocles does not seem to have been a king at all, for his portrait wears no diadema, but Laodice's head does seem to be bound
with the diadema, in the Greek East the invariable sign of royalty.
And indeed her appearance on coins in such a connexion would
scarcely be explicable unless she were of royal parentage. But we
must remain in ignorance whose daughter she was. Von Sallet has
proposed an entirely different interpretation of the coins in question. He thinks that they were issued by Eucratides, not in honour
of his parents, but on the occasion of the marriage of his son
Heliocles (who afterwards succeeded him) with a Laodice, whom
Sallet conjectures to have been daughter of Demetrius by the
daughter of Antiochus III., whom that monarch betrothed to
Demetrius in the course of his Indian campaign. On this hypo-
thesis some recent writers have tried to build further structures
of theory. But it is unfitted to bear such a weight. In its favour
is the one fact that the name Laodice was usual in (not peculiar
to) the Seleucid dynasty of Syria. On the other side are reasons
of more weight. The portraits of Heliocles and Laodice on the
coins are of elderly, not young persons; and it is not easy to see
how Sallet would interpret in the inscriptions which accompany

* See page 19, pl. vi. 9, 10.

the portraits the genitive case in the names of Heliocles and Laodice, unless he understands before them the word υἱός. If any one carefully compares the head of the elder Heliocles (pl. vi. 9), with that of Eucratides (pl. v. 6), and that of the younger Heliocles (pl. vii. 1, 2), he must allow that it resembles Eucratides far more nearly than his son; which may be best accounted for by supposing that the artist constructed the head of the elder Heliocles after his death, on the analogy of that of his son Eucratides.

The wars between Demetrius and Eucratides are mentioned by

Wars of Demetrius and Eucratides.

Justin;* but the statements of this writer must be received with great caution, nor can we believe his assertions that the Indian conquests of Eucratides belong to the end of his reign, or that Demetrius ruled until nearly the same time. For the coins seem to contradict them. The coins of Demetrius come in almost all cases from Bactria, those of Eucratides are very commonly found in the Kabul Valley. The coins of Demetrius bear Greek legends only, with rare exception, while the bronze coins of Eucratides are nearly all bilingual, an indication alike of their later date than the money of Demetrius and that they were issued in India. We therefore, must still retain the opinion that Demetrius ruled only during the early part of the reign of Eucratides in Bactria as well as in India, and that Eucratides was for a great part of his reign lord of India as well as of Bactria and Arachosia. Eucratides founded the city of Eucratidia in Bactria; Demetrius, Demetrias in Arachosia, and Euthydemia in India.

Cunningham places the commencement of the career of Eucratides

---

* " Multa tamen Eucratides bella magna virtute gessit, quibus adtritus cum obsidionem Demetrii regis Indorum pateretur, cum ccc. militibus lx. milia hostium adsiduis eruptionibus vicit. Quinto itaque mense liberatus Indiam in potestatem redegit. Unde cum se reciperet a filio quem socium regni fecerat, in itinere interficitur."—Justin, xli. 6.

Reign of Eucratides. about B.C. 190, and this date must be approximately right.* His reign began brilliantly, and was continued with chequered fortune; but the wide field over which his coins are found,† and their commonness, seems to testify to his great power. We may also remark his assumption of the title Βασιλεὺς μέγας as a clear indication of extensive dominions, and the fact that his types and titles are copied by the kings of Parthia,‡ and by Timarchus, king of Babylon,§ as showing how widely his money circulated. But it appears that towards the end of his reign certain provinces‖ were wrested from him by the Parthians, probably in the time of their great king Mithradates, who came to the throne about B.C. 170. The reign of Eucratides appears to have lasted until the times of two kings, who certainly imitate his money, Plato, whom the date on his unique and remarkable coin shows

Plato. to have ruled in B.C. 165, and Timarchus of Babylon B.C. 162. Plato would seem to have been a mere ephemeral rival, or a revolted satrap of Eucratides.

We must assign to the period of the reign of Eucratides, that is, to the first half of the second century B.C., the

Euthydemus II.
Pantaleon,
Agathocles,
Antimachus I. coins of the kings Euthydemus II., Pantaleon, Agathocles, and Antimachus I. This assignment, which was first made by von Sallet, is on grounds of style quite incontestable. It is impossible, in view of the art

---

* There does not seem to be any conclusive evidence on the point. v. Sallet quotes the imitation of Eucratides' types by certain early Arsacid kings as a proof that Eucratides' reign began early; but the attribution of the early coins of the Arsacidae is a matter of dispute.

† According to Cunningham, they are found at Balkh, in Bokhara; Seistan, the Kabul Valley, &c., and a few in the Panjab.

‡ For instance, Arsaces VI., Mithradates I. See Gardner, *The Parthian Coinage*, p. 31. Other writers attribute these coins to others of the Arsacidae.

§ *B. M. Cat. Seleucidae*, pl. xv. 2, p. 50.

‖ Τήν τε Ἀσπιώνου καὶ τὴν Τουριούαν ἀφῄρηντο Εὐκρατίδην οἱ Παρθυαῖοι: Strabo xl. 11, ed. Kramer. The names seem corrupt, and have been variously amended.

and fabric of the coins of those kings, to give them, as previous
writers, and even Cunningham did, to the earliest days of
Bactrian independence. And the evidence of style is further
confirmed by the consideration that as all these kings reigned
on the south side of the Paropamisus, they cannot be assigned
to an earlier period than that of the Indian conquests of
Demetrius.

This new light is of the utmost importance in the classification
of the earlier Greek kings of India: it entirely destroys an order
which was full of difficulties, and puts in its place one which
is thoroughly intelligible and satisfactory.

The coins of the younger Euthydemus are certainly subsequent
to those of Demetrius, whose types they borrow. There can,
therefore, be no reasonable doubt that this king was either the
younger son of Euthydemus I., or else the son of Demetrius and
grandson of Euthydemus I. As the coins of the younger Euthydemus are not by most writers distinguished from those of the
elder, it is not possible to ascertain their find-spots, or to determine
the locality of his reign; its date would seem to be about B.C. 170.
From the rarity of his coins it may be judged that his reign was
soon brought to an end.

Pantaleon and Agathocles strike with almost identical types.
They both adopt the metal nickel* for their coins, and they alone use
in their legends the square Indian alphabet. They seem, therefore,
to have been closely connected, either brothers, or father and son.
Coins of both are found in the Kabul Valley and the western
Panjab, and those of Agathocles as far south as Kandahar. Pantaleon seems from his portrait to have been the elder of the two, and
the rarity of his coins shows his reign to have been ephemeral.
Agathocles seems to have ruled more widely and longer, and he has

* See Dr. Flight's analysis in *Num. Chron.* 1868, p. 305.

left us in some of his coins valuable materials for the determination of points in his history.

Of the greatest importance is a series of coins,* which indeed we may rather term medals, of the weight of Attic tetradrachms, issued by Agathocles in commemoration of his predecessors in the Greek rule of Bactria. These medals reproduce alike the portraits of these predecessors, and, what is still more unusual, their coin-types, so that only by their style and their inscriptions do they differ from the ordinary coins of those monarchs. The inscriptions run thus :—

Medals struck by Agathocles and Antimachus.

ΑΛΕΞΑΝΔΡΟΥ ΤΟΥ ΦΙΛΙΠΠΟΥ   ΒΑΣΙΛΕΥΟΝΤΟΣ
                                      ΑΓΑΘΟΚΛΕΟΥΣ ΔΙΚΑΙΟΥ
ΑΝΤΙΟΧΟΥ ΝΙΚΑΤΟΡΟΣ   „
ΔΙΟΔΟΤΟΥ ΣΩΤΗΡΟΣ   „
ΕΥΘΥΔΗΜΟΥ ΘΕΟΥ   „

To these we must add the parallel coin of King Antimachus :

ΔΙΟΔΟΤΟΥ ΣΩΤΗΡΟΣ   ΒΑΣΙΛΕΥΟΝΤΟΣ
                                     ΘΕΟΥ ΑΝΤΙΜΑΧΟΥ

I have elsewhere† discussed these medals, the true character of which v. Sallet was the first to establish. They prove that Pantaleon and Agathocles, like the younger Euthydemus, belonged to the faction of Euthydemus I. and Demetrius, and were presumably opposed to Eucratides. Agathocles traces his political pedigree through Euthydemus I., Diodotus, and an Antiochus,‡ to

---

* Pl. iv. 1, 3, xxx. 5, 6.

† *Num. Chron.* 1881, p. 184.

‡ It is disputed which of the three first Antiochi of Syria is the Antiochus Nicator of these coins. None of them seems really to have borne the title: the first was Soter, the second Theos, the third Megas. In favour of Antiochus I., it may be urged that he was the only Antiochus who held undisputed sway in Bactria, and might well be regarded by the Eastern Greeks as full successor of Alexander the Great; also his father Seleucus was called Nicator. In favour of Antiochus II., we have the strong argument that the type of the seated Herakles which is repeated on the Bactrian coin is copied from coins of Syria given by

Alexander the Great himself. Antimachus claims Diodotus as his predecessor. These facts seem to suggest, what is by no means improbable in itself, that Euthydemus II., Pantaleon, and Agathocles were all sons of Demetrius. And possibly, though this is more speculative, Antimachus, as to whose connexions we have no information, was the representative by descent or otherwise of the house of Diodotus.

The types of Antimachus' coins add one more to the few known Types of facts of Greek-Indian history. They are, on the Antimachus. silver coins, Poseidon holding trident and palm; and on the bronze, Victory standing on a ship. There is no mistaking the meaning of these types, which clearly allude to a naval victory won by the king. It might seem at first sight that this victory must have been won on the open sea. But Antimachus' rule never extended to the sea: his coins are found both on the north and the south of the Caucasus, but never south of the Panjab. We must therefore suppose that the naval victory was won on the Indus, or one of its great tributaries; and, indeed, it may easily be understood that the Greeks would place so large a river as the Indus under the sway of Poseidon.

Eucratides was succeeded by his son Heliocles. The coins of this Heliocles : two king are found mostly in Bactria, but also in the classes of coins. Kabul Valley. He is, as Cunningham remarks, the last king who struck to the north of the Indian Caucasus. We may therefore be almost sure that in his reign the nomadic tribes conquered the whole country as far south as the Bamian Pass. The silver coins of Heliocles fall into two classes. The first class consists of coins of the Attic standard of weight, bearing Greek

general consent to Antiochus II. In favour of Antiochus III., the only argument is a passage of Malala (p. 261), where the term Nicator seems to be applied to this king. But this passage is deprived of all weight by the numerous mistakes which it contains. The balance of evidence is greatly in favour of Antiochus I. or II.

legends only. The second class consists of coins of a different weight, which I call the Persian,* which bear bilingual inscriptions and a different portrait of the king. The theory is obvious that the first class was issued by the king while he ruled in Bactria, and the second class at a later period, when he was king only of a corner of India. And it is greatly in favour of this view that the coins of the Bactrian class were largely copied by the barbarous tribes of central Asia, just as the coins of Philip and Alexander were by the Gauls who invaded Macedon about B.C. 290, while those of the Indian class are closely like coins of subsequent Greek kings of the Kabul Valley and India.

Down to the reign of Heliocles, which must be assigned to about **Successors of Heliocles.** B.C. 160—120, we are able to trace with certainty, or little less than certainty, the order of succession of the Greek kings of India. But we now arrive on the verge of a period of uncertainty, where the data are very scanty. In fact, our task would become almost hopeless, were it not that the annals of **Principal information from Chinese sources.** China preserve a general outline of the history of Bactria and India in the account which they give of the wanderings of the nomad nations on the western borders of China, during the second and first centuries B.C. To identify the names of kings and of places as recorded by the Chinese with those which we find on the coins is no easy task, but it is a task which has been attempted, and with some measure of success in the opinion of those best qualified to judge.

The most recent authority who has examined the Chinese evidence **Chinese account of the Yue-chi.** as to the migrations of the Yueh-chi, M. E. Specht,† thus sums it up:—The Yueh-chi were conquered in 201 and 165 B.C. by the Huns, and fled westward, subjugating the Ta-hia of Bactria, and fixing their seat to the north of the Oxus,

* See below, p. lviii .   † *Journal Asiatique*, 8th Ser., vol. ii. p. 348.

where a Chinese ambassador found them in 126 B.C. After that visit they captured Lan-chi, the capital of the Ta-hia. A hundred years later, Khiu-tsiu-kio [Kadphises I.], ruler of the Kushans, one of the Yueh-chi tribes, conquered all the other tribes, invaded the kingdom of the Arsacidae,* seized Kabul and Ki-pin [Cophene], and formed a great kingdom. His son conquered India, and the empire thus founded lasted from the middle of the first to the end of the fourth century.

Who the Ta-hia may be is not clear: they have been identified with the Scythian tribe of the Dahae, but the Chinese description of them—"each town was governed by its magistrate, the population was weak and feared war,"—would not apply to any Scythic race, but would very well apply to the native Bactrians under Greek dominion; and the date at which the Greeks were driven across the Paropamisus, in the reign of Heliocles, would fall not far from B.C. 126.

In the Kabul Valley the Hellenic race held out for a century later, until Kadphises I. led the united tribes of Yueh-chi against them, and, after vanquishing them, ruled the country, at first in conjunction with the last king, Hermaeus, and finally in his place.

The Chinese authorities thus give us two dates of the utmost value for the reconstruction of the history of India and Bactria: the nomad tribes conquered Bactria (Heliocles) about B.C. 125, and India (Hermaeus) about B.C. 25. These dates both suit the numismatic evidence very well. Gen. Cunningham gives Hermaeus to a far earlier period than B.C. 25, assigning him indeed to so early a time as 138—120. But not only does this conflict with historical records, but it is also in collision with numismatic testimony. For Hermaeus was, as all writers agree, the last of the

---

* About B.C. 31, Phraates, with the help of a Scythian army, expelled Tiridates from the government of Parthia.

Greek kings of Kabul. We are therefore obliged to place between Heliocles and him the reigns of all the twenty Greek kings whose coins have come down to us. To cramp all these reigns into the space of thirty years, B.C. 160—130, is an unreasonable proceeding. Moreover the forms of letters on some of the coins, those of Zoilus, Nicias, and Hermaeus, entirely preclude us from assigning them to so early a period as B.C. 130; they must be quite a century later.

The Chinese writers also authorize the supposition that the Scythian race which wrought the ruin of the Greeks was that of the Yueh-chi, who have been identified with the Tochari of Strabo. And the coins, in this confirming Chinese testimony, show that the tribe of Yueh-chi to which Kadphises belonged was the tribe of Kushan, already mentioned on the last page.

This knowledge is valuable; but it leaves us in ignorance on many points. We are still unaware to what tribes belonged the barbarous rulers of India in this age who did not come in with Kadphises. Maues, Azes, and their successors, who established a kingdom in India, as we shall hereafter see, before the days of Hermaeus, do not appear to have been Yueh-chi; and we are quite in doubt as to the connexions of Gondophares and other rulers.

Before proceeding to speak more in detail of the various groups of kings, we will set forth in the form of a chart the general outlines of our historical and geographical knowledge in regard to them :—

CHART TO SHOW EXTENT OF DOMINIONS AND DATES OF GREEK AND SCYTHIC KINGS.

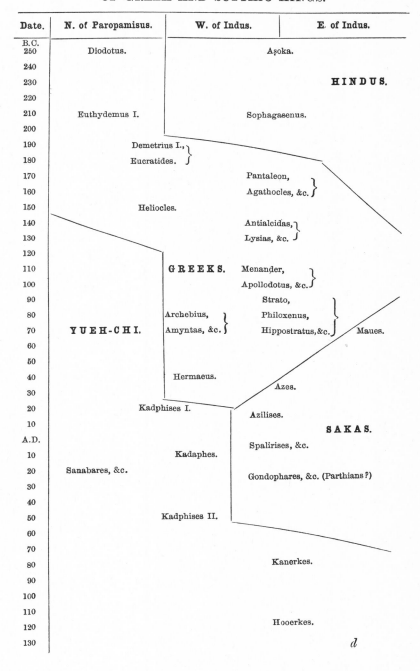

Date.	N. of Paropamisus.	W. of Indus.	E. of Indus.
B.C. 250	Diodotus.	Aṣoka.	
240			
230			**HINDUS.**
220			
210	Euthydemus I.	Sophagasenus.	
200			
190	Demetrius I.,		
180	Eucratides.		
170		Pantaleon,	
160		Agathocles, &c.	
150	Heliocles.		
140		Antialcidas,	
130		Lysias, &c.	
120			
110	**GREEKS.**	Menander,	
100		Apollodotus, &c.	
90		Strato,	
80	Archebius,	Philoxenus,	
70	**YUEH-CHI.**	Amyntas, &c.	Hippostratus, &c.	Maues.
60			
50			
40	Hermaeus.		
30		Azes.	
20	Kadphises I.	Azilises.	
10			**SAKAS.**
A.D.		Spalirises, &c.	
10	Kadaphes.		
20	Sanabares, &c.	Gondophares, &c. (Parthians?)	
30			
40			
50	Kadphises II.		
60			
70			
80		Kanerkes.	
90			
100			
110			
120		Hooerkes.	
130			

d

Leaving out of account the predecessors of Heliocles, we know

Greek Successors of Heliocles;— arrangement.
already of upwards of twenty kings and of two queens who ruled in the Kabul Valley and the Panjab after about B.C. 160, and before the Indo-Scythic conquest of those regions. The orderly arrangement of these rulers is a matter of the utmost difficulty and even of impossibility. The classification of General Cunningham is based on indications so slight that it cannot resist serious criticism: and indeed its validity depends in a great degree on his arrangement of the early kings, which must now be given up in consequence of the readjustment of Pantaleon and Agathocles. Von Sallet so entirely despairs of any reasonable arrangement that he adopts one which is merely alphabetical. All that has been attempted in the present catalogue is to group the kings roughly in something like chronological order, keeping similar types of coin as far as possible together. By means of the Index any king can easily be found, and that is the chief necessity.

It will however be well to set forth briefly what certain data we

Chronological data.
possess for the chronological and geographical assignment of the kings. We will begin with the chronological.

The only one of these later kings who strikes money on the

Date of Antialcidas and Lysias.
Attic standard is Antialcidas, who must therefore be either a contemporary or an immediate successor of Heliocles. And as Antialcidas and Lysias strike some coins in common they also must be contemporaries. A common type of Antialcidas is the pilei of the Dioscuri, which seems to connect him with Eucratides; his portrait also resembles that of Heliocles: he would seem therefore not improbably to belong to the Eucratidian dynasty. The connexion of Lysias is obscure.

There are also a few restrikings which help us in the assign-

Evidence of restrikings.

ment of dates to some of the Greek kings of India. Heliocles restrikes some of the coins of Strato I,* and the name and types of Eucratides are stamped on a piece of Antialcidas,† as well as on some coins which I have assigned to Apollodotus I;‡ but it has been doubted whether these coins of Eucratides were really issued during his lifetime.

Any attempt finally to arrange the kings in dynastic lists by means

Types and legends of coins offer few indications.

of the types and legends which they use is destined to failure. The kings did not inherit these things, but adopted them according to fancy or convenience. One or two instances will be sufficient to establish this. That Heliocles was son and successor of Eucratides is perhaps the most certain fact in Bactrian history. Yet he does not resemble Eucratides in his title ($\delta i\kappa\alpha\iota\sigma$ for $\mu\epsilon\gamma\alpha\varsigma$), he does not wear the same helmet, nor use the same types. In the two last respects Demetrius differs from his father Euthydemus. On the other hand, Diodotus, who revolted against Antiochus II., retained the types of the Syrian king. These instances are sufficient to prove that identity of types between two kings is no proof of their relation to one another, nor is divergence of types any proof that they were not related. Still less can we draw any conclusions from the form of a helmet or the adoption of a title.

Perhaps the most suggestive approximation of types is that which appears when we compare the rare coins of Agathocleia, wife of Strato, with those of Euthydemus. They bear on the reverse the same type, Herakles seated, which is not usual in the Bactrian series. It is almost certain that Agathocleia must have been a king's daughter and heiress; otherwise, as we know from the coins

---

* Strato also restrikes coins of Heliocles.

† Sallet, p. 298.

‡ Cunningham, in *Num. Chron.* 1869, p. 226.

of Greek kings, her name would scarcely have appeared on the coin. That she was descended from Euthydemus is therefore very likely. We have already seen that king Agathocles was probably son of Euthydemus; Agathocleia may well have been his grand-daughter, or otherwise related to him. But in this kind of argument there are obviously the greatest risks; and we will attempt it in no second instance.

A large find of coins of the kings from Heliocles to Hermaeus

Evidence of Sonipat find. was discovered some years ago at Sonipat;* and no less than 703 specimens have been weighed by Gen. Cunningham, who has acutely suggested that the order of the reigns may be gathered by a consideration of the amount of weight lost in circulation by the coins of different kings, those kings whose coins are most worn being naturally supposed to be the earliest. The loss is as follows :—

Heliocles, 5·43 gr.	Philoxenus, 3·77 gr.
Apollodotus, 4·57 gr.	Menander, 3·72 gr.
Strato, 4·56 gr.	Diomedes, 3·39 gr.
Antimachus II., 4·48 gr.	Amyntas, 3·30 gr.
Antialcidas, 4·10 gr.	Hermaeus, 3·20 gr.
Lysias, 3·73 gr.	

In this calculation it is assumed that the normal standard for hemidrachms is 37 grains, and that all kings minted up to that standard. This is, of course, not certain; nevertheless, the results of the test so nearly agree with the testimony of style, that we can scarcely be wrong in regarding the above order as approximately correct; only Antialcidas and Lysias should not be placed so late.

Among all these kings, two only, Apollodotus and Menander, are

Menander. known to us from other sources. Menander is identified with the Milinda of the Buddhist work

* *Num. Chron.* 1872, p. 161.

" Milinda-praṣna," which records not only that he was born at the sub-Caucasian Alexandria, but that he was a just and powerful ruler, and a convert to the Buddhist religion. Strabo* says that he was reported to have crossed the river Hypanis eastward and penetrated as far as the Isamus, but as we are ignorant where the Isamus was, this does not greatly add to our knowledge. Plutarch† records that as a ruler he was noted for justice; and that when he died many cities were anxious to possess his ashes—a curious tale, which is considered by Prinsep to indicate a Buddhist source. The extraordinary abundance and wide distribution of his silver coins is well known. They were current, with those of Apollodotus, at Barygaza, many years after his death,‡ and are still abundantly found over a wide region, including Kabul, Jalalabad, Peshawar, Mathura, and Rampur. They are not brought from Kandahar or Seistan. " From this evidence," says Cunningham,§ " it is certain that Menander could not have possessed any part of Arachosia or Drangiana, and that his dominions to the west of the Indus must have been confined to the Kabul Valley and Eastern Afghanistan."

The coins which bear the name of Apollodotus fall into two classes : these are distinguished in the Catalogue.

Apollodotus.

The second class are of later and poorer style; and on them the king usually bears the title of Philopator. General Cunningham says ‖ that the Philopator coins are found only in the Panjab and N.-W. India, while the others are found over a much wider area, including the " Upper Kabul Valley in the north, Kandahar and Roh in the west and east, and Sindh in the south." The evidence, on the whole, indicates that there were two kings of the name of Apollodotus, of whom the later, Philopator, was

---

* xi. 11. 1.   † *De Repub. Ger.*, p. 821.
‡ *Periplus maris Erythraei*, c. 47, ed. Müller.
§ *Num. Chron.* 1870, p. 221.   ‖ Ibid., 1870, p. 77.

colleague of his father, the earlier, and his successor in some part of his dominions. And this probability will be raised almost to a certainty if we suppose that the restriking of Apollodotus' coins with the name of Eucratides took place in the life-time of the latter; since the coins which bear the legend Philopator cannot be brought within a considerable distance of the reign of Eucratides.

We have thus but slight indications, beside those of art and fabric, to help us in determining the dates of the kings from Heliocles to Hermaeus. Nor have we safer data for their geographical assignment. The find-spots of their coins have never been recorded with completeness or accuracy. And the monograms which have been supposed to contain the names of mints have not been satisfactorily read, in spite of the diligent efforts of General Cunningham, whose want of success* in the matter seems to prove that success is not possible, at least in the present state of knowledge on the subject. And the details of the types adopted by various kings help us no more in determining the locality of their rule than in assigning their line of descent.

Geographical data ; find-spots, and monograms.

We can, however, make a few rough divisions of territory. Heliocles and his predecessors minted, as we have seen, in Bactria, his successors only on the south of the Indian Caucasus. And further, it would seem that the Panjab and the Kabul Valley were frequently in different hands. Thus the coins of Archebius and Amyntas seem to be found in Kabul, and not to the east of the Indus ; and those of Hermaeus are far commoner in the same district than in the Panjab. On the other hand, the coins of kings Philoxenus, Strato, and

---

* Gen. Cunningham's readings have not been accepted by the best numismatists. Von Sallet remarks, " Such interpretations and experiments have too weak a basis to serve for historical investigations." See also the remarks of M. Chabouillet in the *Revue Numism.*, 1867, p. 403.

Hippostratus are chiefly found to the east of Jalalabad. A more exact statement could only be made after many years' study on the spot.

The recorded find-spots of coins are however sufficient to give us an idea of the extent of the Greek kingdom in India. Cunningham states that coins of Apollodotus are found as far south as Kandahar and Sindh, and those of Menander as far east as Mathura on the Jamna. And there appear to be proofs in Sanskrit literature* that a Greek ruler (perhaps Menander) besieged Ayodhya and Pātali-putra (Oudh and Patna). But these expansions were temporary, and there is no doubt that the only districts which were really Hellenized were the Kabul Valley and the western Panjab.

Coins of Antialcidas, Apollodotus, Menander, Lysias, Antimachus II., Diomedes, Archebius, and Hermaeus, were found by Masson† in the course of a few years at Beghram; and since his time coins of Epander, Dionysius, Zoilus, Amyntas, and other kings have been found in the same region, if not on the same site. The kings mentioned, and probably others of Greek race, must all have reigned in the Kabul Valley.

With the Greek kings we have placed one of Indian name,
Ranjabala.   Ranjabala, whose coins resemble those of Strato, and show him to have been nearly contemporary with that king. He may have been a satrap of Strato, who asserted his independence. His coins have been found in the eastern Panjab and at Mathura‡ in company with some of Strato.

* Cunningham, in *Num. Chron.* 1870, p. 224.

† See his important list of coins found at Beghram, in the *Journ. As. Soc. Bengal*, 1836, p. 537.

‡ Cunningham, *J. A. S. B.* 1854, p. 691. In this paper it is suggested that Ranjabala may be identical with Rājapāla, a king of the lunar race of Dehli, and that Zeionises may be Jīvana Rāja of the same dynasty. The reasons against these identifications are, however, very strong.

The barbarous kings who make their appearance in India after

Scythic Kings. the destruction of the Greek kingdoms present even greater difficulties of arrangement than do the Greek kings themselves. Between the eastern expedition of

Difficulties of Chronology. Antiochus III., in B.C. 208, and the era of Kanerkes, which may be taken as fixed* to A.D. 78, there is no absolutely fixed point, and we are reduced to arguments of mere probability.

Of all the coins of the barbarous rulers, those of Maues are

Maues. the earliest in style. Von Sallet remarks that the copper coins of this king are like those of Demetrius and Apollodotus, and belong to a period not much later than that of those kings. In the forms of Greek letters, and the style of art, his coins are superior not only to those of Hermaeus, but also to those of kings such as Zoilus and Nicias. It is impossible to place King Maues at a later date than the middle of the first century B.C. And it is an interesting fact, vouched for by Cunningham, that his coins are found in the Panjab only, especially the N.W. part of it, and not in Afghanistan. We must suppose that he ruled over some Scythic invaders, who had entered India not through the Kabul Valley, but through Kashmir or Nepal, while the country to the west of Peshawar was ruled by contemporary Greek kings. At present the Passes between Kashmir and Yarkand are but little used, but it is stated that the Karakoram Pass is open all the year round; and the trade between India and Yarkand by that route has of late years greatly increased. And we know that in old times Kashgar was far more thickly peopled than at present. It is also a matter of history that Nepal has more than once been invaded by Chinese armies. It would appear likely that at the time of the conquest of Bactria by the

* See below, p. li.

Yueh-chi, as to which something has been said already, about B.C. 130, some tribe of that race or some other Scythic horde passed southward through Kashmir or Nepal; and after imbibing something of Greek civilization, and learning the Greek language, succeeded during the decline of the Greek power after Menander in establishing a kingdom to the east of the Indus, of which Maues was the first ruler.

Azes was, according to general consent, the successor of Maues.

Azes, Azilises. Von Sallet suggests that he was his son, and reads on coins of Azes, with hesitation, the legend YMAV▯, which may stand for υἱὸς Μαύου. Azes was certainly of later date than Maues, as the forms of his inscriptions and the art of his coins testify. His money also is not found to the west of Jalalabad; it is therefore likely that he did not greatly extend the dominions of Maues, though the extraordinary number of his coins testifies to his wealth and power. Azes strikes in conjunction with Aspavarma, Azilises, Vonones, and Spalirises, and Vonones in conjunction with Spalahores and Spalagadames. This shows that Azes, Azilises, Vonones, and the Spalirises group, of whom we shall speak presently, all belong to one time and to a single group of kings. But Vonones and Spalirises seem, from the find-spots of their coins, certainly to have reigned in Kabul: they may have ruled there and been tributary to Azes; but how they coexisted with the latest Greek kings and the invaders from Bactria, the kings of the Kadphises line, we are unable to determine.

Of the relations between themselves of the kings composing this

Vonones, Spalirises, &c. group the legends of their coins enable us to judge in some measure :—

1. Βασιλέως βασιλέων μεγάλου ᾿Αζου = name and titles of the Strategos Aspavarma.

e

2. Βασιλέως. βασιλέων μεγάλου "Αζου=Βασιλέως βασιλέων μεγάλου 'Αζιλίσου.*

3. Βασιλέως βασιλέων μεγάλου 'Ονώνου=Βασιλέως ἀδέλφου δικαίου Σπαλαόρου.

4. Βασιλέως βασιλέων μεγάλου 'Ονώνου=Σπαλαόρου υἱοῦ δικαίου Σπαλαγαδάμου.

5. Βασιλέως βασιλέων μεγάλου Σπαλιρίσου = Βασιλέως μεγάλου Σπαλιρίσου.

6. Βασιλέως μεγάλου Σπαλιρίσου=Βασιλέως μεγάλου "Αζου.†

7. Βασιλέως ἀδέλφου Σπαλιρίσου = Βασιλέως ἀδέλφου δικαίου Σπαλιρίσου.

8. Σπαλύριος δικαίου ἀδέλφου τοῦ βασιλέως = Σπαλαόρου υἱοῦ δικαίου Σπαλαγαδάμου.

9. Vonones and Azes (undescribed coin, said to be in Gen. Cunningham's possession).

The evidence afforded by these legends is valuable, but not so decisive as it might at first sight appear, and capable of being variously construed. Some points, however, are clear. Four kings of the set assume the title King of Kings (Azes, Azilises, Vonones and Spalirises), but they do not do so in succession ; Azes seems content to share the title in a friendly way with Azilises and Spalirises, at any rate.† Spalirises was brother of a king, but of which king does not appear. Spalahores is also brother of a king, and he and his son Spalagadames strike in conjunction with Vonones. Spalyris is another brother, and at one time Spalagadames strikes in conjunction with him. As close alliances of this kind scarcely occurred in antiquity, except between members of one family, we may regard it

* These reverse titles are really written in Indian. I give, for convenience, the Greek equivalents.

† This is sufficient proof that the assumption of the title Βασιλεὺς βασιλέων, 'Mahārāja adhirāja', does not imply a claim to general supremacy.

as probable, if not certain, that all the kings of the group were related one to the other. In that case it is likely that Azilises, Vonones, Spalirises, Spalahores, and Spalyris were all sons of Azes, and Spalagadames his grandson. Aspavarma was a mere general or satrap of Azes—perhaps, as his name seems to show, of Hindu descent. The kingdom of Maues lasted in the hands of these rulers from before the middle of the first century B.C. at least until A.D. 20 or 30, spreading with time over a larger and larger area. It must have been put down by the growing power of the kings of the Kushan tribe, perhaps by Kadphises II.

We have coins of several other kings in India of the same period,

Kings with Parthian names. who do not appear to have been connected with either the dynasty of Kadphises or that of Azes. The only tie which connects them together is the Parthian character of their names, and in most cases of their coin-types. Some both in name and portrait, Pacores and Arsaces, for instance, are thoroughly Parthian. It is to be observed that under Mithradates and his warlike successors the Parthians had extended their empire into Bactria, and driven back the invading Scythians. Some scions of the royal Arsacid stock, or mere Parthian noblemen, may have gained a footing in India and maintained themselves in opposition to the Scythic kings.

The most important king of the Parthian class is Gondophares,

Gondophares and Abdagases. with whom goes Abdagases, who on his coins calls himself the nephew of Gondophares. The names of these rulers fortunately occur in the legends dating from the third century A.D., which record the visit of S. Thomas to India, * con-

---

* Cunningham, in *Journ. As. Soc. Bengal*, vol. xxiii. Cf. also Gutschmid, *Rhein. Mus.* 1864, p. 161, and von Sallet in *Zeitschr. f. Num.*, 1880, p. 296. Gutschmid shows that Gaspard, one of the three kings of the Christian legend, is identical with Gondophares.

taining indeed much that is untrustworthy, but also a basis of fact.
S. Thomas is represented as converting Gundaphorus, his brother
Gad, possibly the Orthagnes mentioned below, and his sister's son
Labdanes, which last name seems to be a corruption of Abdagases.
Where these rulers lived is not very clear. The legend, however, may
furnish some ground for assigning them to the period of S. Thomas,
that is, the first century A.D. More trustworthy than an early
Christian legend should be the inscription at Takht-i-Bahi, if it could
be read with certainty. Professor Dowson renders thus : * " In the
26th year of the great king Gondophares, on the third day of the
month Vaiṣākha, (year) one hundred of the Samvatsara." Unfortunately, doubt hangs alike over the reading of name and date, nor
can the era be identified, for Samvatsara means merely era. All
that we can be sure of is that Gondophares did *not* reign in
the hundredth year of the Ṣaka era, by which Kanerkes and his
successors (see p. li) date their inscriptions; for the style of his
coins forbids us to place them as late as A.D. 178. If the name of
the king be rightly read it will prove that Gondophares reigned
in the neighbourhood of Peshawar; but even this is not certain.

A silver coin of Gondophares discovered by v. Sallet, and figured in
our plate xxxiii. 2, may perhaps give us a clue to his date. It is of
the types of Arsacid silver coins, and especially reminds us of a coin of
Mithradates II. (B.C. 90 or 80), which has similar types on both sides†—
on one the head of the king; on the other the king seated, holding
an eagle, crowned by a City, who stands behind him. And this last
mentioned type seems not to recur in the Arsacid coinage, so that it
would seem likely that Gondophares actually copied it from the coinage of Mithradates. In the inscription of Gondophares' coin we find
the epithet αὐτοκρατώρ, which is found on the money of only two

* *Journ. R. As. Soc.*, 1875, p. 379.
† Gardner, *Parthian Coinage*, pl. ii. 19.

Arsacid kings—Sinatroces, B.C. 76 to 69, and Phraates IV., A.D. 8—11. This particular coin of Gondophares then would seem to have been struck not later than the middle of the first century A.D. The period mentioned would suit the other coins of Gondophares.

That Orthagnes was a brother of Gondophares rests on a reading

Orthagnes, Arsaces, Zeionises. of his coins proposed by Gen. Cunningham. The supposition has nothing improbable in it; the type of Victory which appears on his coins being also found on those of Gondophares and Abdagases. If it be well founded, it will clearly prove the Parthian origin of the dynasty of Gondophares, Orthagnes connecting him with other Indian kings of Parthian type such as Pacores,* Arsaces θεός and Arsaces δίκαιος. All these rulers must have been contemporary with the great time of the Parthian empire. To the same period will be assigned also Zeionises, who on his coins calls himself by the modest title of Satrap.

With regard to the seat of the power of these Indo-Parthian

Dominions of these kings. kings we have a little information. The coins of Gondophares were found in plenty at Beghram by Masson, and his small rude silver coins in the Panjab; while those of Orthagnes are said by Gen. Cunningham to come from Seistan and Kandahar, and those of Abdagases (with legend Sasasa) from Western Panjab. These facts seem to point to an extensive dominion, and confirm the testimony of the anonymous Egyptian merchant,† who informs us of the existence of a Parthian realm in the neighbourhood of the mouth of the Indus, in the reign of Vespasian.

The silver coins of Sanabares, of which there is a specimen in the

---

* Not Pacorus. Almost all the names of the kings of this class end in —es ; I have therefore kept that ending in doubtful cases, such as Maues and Spalirises.

† *Periplus maris Eryth.*, c. 38. Cf. Mommsen, *Röm. Geschichte*, vol. v., p. 352.

Sanabares. British Museum (pl. xxiii. 10), have been given by v. Sallet to about the year A.D. 80, and have been compared as contemporary with money of the Arsacid king Vologeses III.* of that period. But the portrait of Sanabares, though it resembles that of Vologeses, is still more like that of Mithradates II., the helmet having cheek-pieces like the helmet of the latter monarch, while the style of work is very superior to anything known in Parthia in the days of Vologeses. Mr. Thomas had read on the Museum specimen the date ᒥIᛏ, which he interpreted as implying the 313th year of the Seleucid, and first of the Christian era. But this reading is now disputed,† and cannot be insisted on. But if it is given up we should be still inclined to place Sanabares at about the beginning of the Christian era. Sanabares does not use Indian characters in his legends, but either Greek or Pehlvi, and four of the five coins of his in the British Museum came from Persia. It is therefore likely that this king ruled exclusively or principally to the north of the Indian Caucasus.

On referring to the coins of the Arsacidae, we find that in that **Epigraphy of these kings.** series the square ▫ and ⊏ come in some twenty years B.C. On the other hand, the square Ш ‡ does not take the place of Ω until 8 A.D. It is quite in keeping with these facts that Maues uses round letters only; Azes, Azilises, Spalirises and their contemporaries, use the square ▫ with Ω; Gondophares and Abdagases use the forms ▫ and Ш. We have thus a series of kings covering the period B.C. 50 to A.D. 50. The date of Pacores

* *Zeitschrift f. Num.*, 1879, p. 356. The text reads 'Vologeses I.'; following the erroneous numbering of Prokesch-Osten.

† On other specimens the letters take the form ᛏ⅂ᛏ &c. They may have no meaning.

‡ In the text this form is used in the legend of King Nicias, who certainly reigned earlier than 8 A.D. But on the actual coins of that king the letter is rounder; and of earlier type.

and Arsaces is not easy to fix, but must fall during this period. It is, however, noteworthy, as von Sallet points out, that the coin of Arsaces θεὸς bears precisely the same types as one of Maues.

The nameless king, who calls himself merely Soter Megas,
The nameless king. naturally gives us no clue in his inscription to decide his affinities. Some of his coins are in type and style closely like those of Abdagases ; and as he also makes use of the form Ш, he must be of about the same period as that king, A.D. 30–50. His coins are found in great numbers in the Kabul Valley. He may possibly have been a member of the Kadphises dynasty.

After the kings of Parthian character we must mention some
Heraüs and the Sakas. others whose types are not dissimilar, yet who appear to be of Scythian race. Among these the most important is Heraüs, whose remarkable coin (pl. xxiv. 7) throws some light over the history of this troubled time. Of late the reading of the legend Τυραννοῦντος Ἡράου Σάκα κοιράνου has been disputed, but without solid reason, except as regards the last word. This may with equal exactness and probability be read κορράνου; but even if we do thus read it, the presence of the τυραννοῦντος, which is quite undisputed, proves that unusual Greek words may be expected at this time, and suggests that κορράνου may be a corruption of κοιράνου. The reading HPAOY is allowed by Mr. Thomas ; but he now disputes the important word Saka, reading instead of it the unintelligible words ΣΑΝ ΑΒ.* But we must point out that on the Brit. Mus. coin the third letter of the word is not formed like the N's, of which there are four in the inscription, but like a retrograde И, which is on late Parthian and Bactrian coins an ordinary shape of K : see pls. xxv, vi. *passim.* Thus there seems to

---

* A similar coin in the possession of M. Tiesenhausen seems to read ΣΑИΑΒ ΚΟΓΓΑИΟΥ. See Thomas, *R. A. S. Journal*, 1883, p. 75.

be at present no sufficient reason for doubting that Heraüs calls himself a Saka king; and we thus gain a confirmation of the statement of ancient historians, that that race was prominent in the conquest of India from the Greeks. But Heraüs probably ruled, like other kings of the class, to the north of the Caucasus.

Similar in type of head to Heraüs is Hyrcodes, one of whose ordinary

Hyrcodes and others. types, that of the half-horse, is taken from silver coins of the early Antiochi of Syria, which circulated in Bactria. Wilson states that most of his coins come from the Bactrian side of the Caucasus; Mr. Thomas,* that they belong to Kerman. At page 119 of the Catalogue will be found a few coins of the same class which seem to bear the names of other kings; but these legends may be mere blundered attempts to produce some more intelligible name.

Finally, we have to speak of a well-defined group of kings which

Kadphises I. and successors. takes its rise with that Kozulo Kadphises who appears on coins as colleague and successor of Hermaeus. His date must be the last quarter of the first century B.C.

We do not know to what branch of the widely extended race of Sakas, or nomads, Maues and his successors belonged. But we have reason to think that the group at present discussed were kings of the Yueh-chi, who are identified by Cunningham with the Tochari, and that they belonged to the Kushan branch of that tribe.

We have already seen how Kadphises led the Yueh-chi, about B.C. 25, southward across the Paropamisus and conquered Hermaeus, whom he reduced to a state of vassalage. Under his successors the dominions of the Yueh-chi went on increasing. Probably he was succeeded by the king who bears the very similar name of Kozola

---

* On a coin probably similar to our pl. xxiv. 13, Mr. Thomas reads Guāʿh in Pehlvi characters (*Sassanian Inscriptions*, p. 10). Our coin is not sufficiently complete for me to be sure of the reading.

Kadaphes, who on his money calls himself the ruler of the Kúshans. The portrait of this ruler on the coins bears so strong a resemblance to that of Augustus that it seems all but certain that he must have reigned at the very beginning of the Christian era. That he succeeded the first Kadphises is very probable, and it is equally probable that he was succeeded by the second, who on his coins calls himself Ooemo Kadphises, and whose reign brings us down to the accession of Kanerkes in A.D. 78. We thus have a succession of princes of the same or nearly the same name extending over 100 years, and it is hard to believe that they do not represent a dynasty which reigned in the Kabul Valley.

Kadaphes, Kadphises II.

We have on a copper-plate from Manikyala (Taxila) a record, wherein a satrap called Liako Kusuluko dates from the 78th year of the great king Moga. It seems not unlikely that the satrap in question may be Kozola Kadaphes, and perhaps still more probable that the great king Moga is Maues. Kadaphes, who probably reigned at the very beginning of the Christian era, may well be placed seventy-eight years later than the accession of Maues, which must be placed not so late as the middle of the first century B.C. But of course it is all but impossible that Maues can have himself reigned seventy-eight years. The reference must be not to the year of his reign, but to an era established by him.

Inscription from Taxila.

The evidence derived from the style and epigraphy of coins seems to show that Kadphises I. and Kadaphes ruled but a part of N.-W. India. When Kadphises came in as an invader from the north, he found Hermaeus ruling in the Kabul Valley, and reduced him to a state of dependence. At the same time Azes was probably ruler of the Panjab; and perhaps some of the later Greek rulers, such as Hippostratus, still held rule on the lower Indus. When Hermaeus died no Greek succeeded him, but Kadphises occupied his place. Kadaphes, or the nameless

Spread of Yueh-chi in India.

f

king, must have succeeded Kadphises: their contemporaries must
have been Azilises, Spalirises and Gondophares. That the coins of

They become dominant under Kadphises II.
Gondophares and of the nameless king are alike found in abundance at Beghram, while those of Kadaphes are not abundant, seems to show that the
Yueh-chi did not rapidly extend their dominion in India, but met
at first with formidable rivals in the descendants of Azes. Only on
the accession of the second Kadphises did the power of the invaders
become altogether predominant. It appears that under him and
his successors it was supreme in all N.-W. India; and Greeks,
Parthians, and the race of Azes alike disappear from history as
reflected in the coins.

Kadphises II., Ooemo Kadphises, was a wealthy monarch, and the

Successors of Kadphises II., Kanerkes and Hooerkes.
founder of a powerful line of Scythic kings, as to whom inscriptions give us some information. His date is about the middle of the first century A.D.
His successors are the kings called on their coins
Kanerkes and Hooerkes, and in the records Kanishka and Huvishka.
Their rule comprised the whole of N.-W. India and the Kabul Valley.

The date of these kings was a matter of uncertainty until the

Their date.
brilliant conjecture of Mr. Fergusson * as to the origin and use of the Saka era settled the matter.
Mr. Fergusson's theory is accepted by most Sanskrit scholars, and
the numismatic evidence in its favour is so overwhelming, that the
numismatist cannot hesitate to join them; in fact, v. Sallet had before
the publication of Mr. Fergusson's paper assigned Kanerkes to the
same period into which he falls on the theory proposed in that paper,
and that on numismatic evidence only. The new theory is that the
Saka era starts from the date not of the destruction of the Sakas,

---

* *On the Saka, Samvat and Gupta Eras, J. R. A. S.* 1880, p. 259. Cf. Max
Müller, *India—What can it teach us?* p. 291.

but of the establishment of their empire in India under Kanerkes. *
It is fixed to A.D. 78. The dates at Mathura and elsewhere are said
to be as follows (Thomas: *Ancient Indian Weights*, p. 46, and *Jainism*,
p. 10) :—

KING.	SAKA YEAR.	YEAR A.D.
Kanerkes,	9, 11, 18, 28	87—106.
Hooerkes,	33, 39, 47, 48, 51	111—129.
Vasu Deva,	44, 83, 87, 98	122—176.

The evidence of finds confirms this assignment of dates. In a
tope at Ahin Posh near Jalalabad, Mr. Simpson found together the
following gold coins : —

10 coins of Kanerkes, 6 of Kadphises, 1 of Hooerkes.

1 of Domitian, 1 of Trajan, 1 of Sabina.
The reigns of the Roman imperial persons cover the period
A.D. 81-136; and this proves that the deposit cannot have been
buried until about A.D. 130,† probably in the reign of Hooerkes.

It is true that in the Manikyala tope there were found with coins
of Kanerkes some worn consular denarii which belong to the period
before Augustus,‡ but it is more than probable that these coins
were not buried till a long time after their issue.

It seems to be universally allowed that the Kanerkes and Hooerkes
of the coins are the Kanishka and Huvishka of inscriptions, and that
these were successive kings of the Kabul Valley and the Panjab.

Vasu Deva. But the Vasu Deva of the inscriptions, who is supposed to correspond to the Bazodeo of the coins, is
a more mysterious personage. He overlaps in the dates Huvishka,

---

* Or, perhaps, Kadphises II.; as it is Kadphises who begins the issue of Indo-
Scythic gold coins : and Kanerkes' earliest date is the year 9.

† Sabina came to the throne in 128. The coin of her issue, now preserved in
the British Museum, is not as stated by previous writers "much worn," but seems
to have greatly suffered, whether in ancient or modern times, by being exposed to
heat. The coin of Trajan is worn. Cf. *J. R. A. Soc.* 1880, p. 266.

‡ *Journ. As. Soc. Bengal*, iii. p. 34.

and appears to have reigned for no less a period than fifty-four years.
Indeed, if one inscription be rightly read, he sometimes dates from
year 5 of the era,* which will give to his reign the impossible length
of 94 years. Prof. Dowson therefore suggests that Vasu Deva may
have been the name given by their Indian subjects to kings of the
Kanerkes dynasty. In favour of this view it may be remarked that
the words Vasu Deva occur in Sanskrit letters on coins of various
periods and classes; and the supposed Greek equivalent BAZOΔHO
occurs only on Indo-Scythic coins of semi-barbarous fabric.

The coins of Vasu Deva are succeeded by a large variety of copies,
some of fairly good style, others of barbarous work, neither class
bearing intelligible legends. Some of these, in copper, were usually
given to an imaginary king Ooer Kenorano, such being their legend.
Von Sallet has, however, conjectured that as there are no gold coins
with the legend Ooer Kenorano, and no copper bearing the legend
Ooerke Korano, the copper coins above mentioned must have been
struck by king Hooerkes. This conjecture is strongly confirmed by
the discovery in the Museum series of coins † in all respects similar
to those reading Ooer Kenorano but reading clearly Ooerke Korano.
But in fact the difference between the two legends is almost evanes-
cent, N in the one taking the place of K in the other; however,
in the inscriptions of this class these two letters are constantly
confounded.‡

The gold coins which repeat barbarously the legends and types of
Vasu Deva become eventually of thin fabric and cup-like shape, like
some of the issues of Byzantium of the ninth and subsequent centuries. But they must be earlier than that period, and are perhaps
copied from the concave coins of the class struck at Persepolis
during Parthian supremacy.

* Cunningham, *Archaeological Reports*, iii. 30. Dowson, *J.R.A.S.* vii. p. 381.
† Pages 156-8. ‡ See above, p. xlvii.

The whole class of Indo-Scythic gold coins appears as a most remarkable phenomenon amid the coins of India, especially as gold coins are entirely wanting in the Greek-Indian issues after the time of Eucratides. The line of descent of the new issue must be traced not through the gold money of Alexander, which perhaps still circulated in southern Asia, but through the Roman aurei which were first issued in abundance by Augustus, and which at the beginning of the Christian era made their way into India, where they have been found in conjunction with coins of Kadphises and Kanerkes. In weight the Indo-Scythic coins nearly correspond to the Roman.

II. Inscriptions.

The inscriptions on the coins contained in this volume are of the following kinds:—

(1) Greek language in Greek characters. On the coins of earlier kings, from Diodotus to Demetrius, Greek legends only are employed. After that time we usually find Greek on one side of the coin only. It is, however, quite evident that the Greek letters and the Greek language were generally understood in northern India and in Kabul as late as the second century of our era. This fact, clearly established by the testimony of coins, confirms the otherwise not trustworthy testimony of Philostratus, who represents that Apollonius of Tyana, when he visited India, had no difficulty in making himself generally understood by speaking Greek. In the Hindu revival under the Guptas the Greek language was probably swept away with other traces of Greek culture. Notable is the use by some of the later rulers of poetical Greek words like κοίρανος, τυραννέων and ἀνίκητος.

Greek language.

(2) Indian language in native characters. These last are of two sorts. The square letters of the so-called Indian Pali are used by Pantaleon and Agathocles only; the

Indian language.

more cursive characters, called Arian Pali, are used by all the other kings down to the latest times. In the case of the edicts of Aṣoka, the Arian characters are used only in the Kabul Valley, and the Indian characters elsewhere; and this fact shows, what is proved in many other ways, how completely the Greek and Scythian power in India centred in the Kabul Valley.

The language which I have called by the general name of Indian is a debased form of Sanskrit or Pali. To fix authoritatively the readings of words in this language is impossible except to a Pali scholar. I have therefore given, in nearly all cases, the readings of previous writers, unless they seemed to me to conflict with the clear testimony of the coins; in which case (a very rare one) I have ventured on innovation. In the cases where it was necessary to decide between various authorities, I have sometimes had the advantage of the advice of Mr. Cecil Bendall, who has kindly allowed me to profit by his wider knowledge of Sanskrit. Still more have I regarded any philological criticism of the forms presented by the coin-legends as lying outside my task. Such criticism might well form a supplement to M. Senart's valuable papers on the language of the Aṣoka edicts in vols. xv. and xvi. of the *Journal Asiatique*, but in a numismatic work it would be altogether out of place. And this is clearly a task which could only be attempted with advantage by a highly-trained Sanskritist.

The system here adopted in transliteration of Pali inscriptions is the same as is used in other Museum Catalogues, and nearly identical with that used by Prof. M. Williams in his Lexicon and Grammar.

To the letters in which these inscriptions are written I have paid **Forms of Indian letters.** closer attention, palæography being perhaps more nearly related to archæology than to philology. To determine their forms requires care and a practised eye rather than wide linguistic knowledge. I have drawn up a table of Arian Pali letters used on the coins, after careful comparison of the authoritative tables drawn up by Gen. Cunningham (see p. lxx). All the letters in the table have been cut upon types; so that printing in this alphabet will in future be comparatively easy. With the square or Indian Pali characters I have not concerned myself, as they occur on so few coins.

(3) Scythic language in Greek characters. These are the inscriptions on coins of the late kings of the Kanerkes group, such as **PAO, NANO, KOZOVΛO, KOPANO**, and more especially the names of deities on the reverses. These words, so far as at present identified, are of non-Scythic origin, borrowed from the languages of India, Persia, and Greece, and only bearing the Scythian stamp in their termination **O**, and in modifications of the forms of words.

Scythic language.

Lists of Greek, Scythic and Indian words will be found in the *Index of Inscriptions;* and renderings of the last-mentioned in the table at p. lxxii.

III.—MONOGRAMS.

In the field of coins of all periods is a prodigious number of monograms and detached letters, sometimes Greek and sometimes of the Arian Pali class. If these could be read and interpreted, there can be no doubt that they would afford us most valuable information. But they present the greatest difficulties.

Gen. Cunningham has well remarked, in regard to some of the Greek monograms, that their constant recurrence during successive reigns proves that they cannot denote monetary magistrates, but must stand for mints. There is reason in this; but when the writer goes further, and tries to identify the various mints which they respectively represent, we, like most students of these coins both in England and abroad, are unable to follow him. While therefore we must acknowledge the

Difficulties of interpretation.

possibility that many of the Greek monograms may stand for the names of mints, we must stop short at that point. Nor does there seem any probability that we shall advance further, until the find-spots of Bactrian and Indian coins are far more exactly recorded than they have hitherto been. The monograms and letters of the Pali alphabet do not recur in the same way as the Greek, but vary far more; and it does not seem probable that they stand for mints. They may stand for the names of magistrates, for the date or number of the issue, or they may have been used for some other purpose which has not yet been guessed. Perhaps, in these circumstances, it may seem superfluous to record them, as has been done in this Catalogue; but it is impossible to be sure that valuable information will not some day be extracted from them.

IV. TYPES.

The types which appear on the coins described in the present volume are most interesting from the point of view of art and mythology; but it is to be regretted that they furnish us with but little historical information. We have already noted the futility of trying to determine the genealogy or the dominions of the Greek kings by means of the types of their coins; and the same holds true, in scarcely less degree, in regard to the kings of Scythic race. It is a remarkable fact that throughout the period of which we treat there seem to have been in N.-W. India artists capable of designing original types for coins, so that the necessity for a slavish copying of foreign coins, which gives valuable material to the historian, does not seem to have arisen.

In the types used by Greek kings we find great variety, and they

Types of Greek kings.

open to us quite a new chapter of Greek art, affording fresh proof of the remarkable originality

of the artists of the Hellenistic age.   In regard to their style, we may
note two points :—(1) The extraordinary realism of their portraiture.
The portraits of Demetrius (pl. ii. 9), of Antimachus (v. 1), and of
Eucratides (v. 7), are among the most remarkable which have come
down to us from antiquity, and the effect of them is heightened in
each case by the introduction of a peculiar and strongly-charac-
teristic head-dress, which is rendered with scrupulous exactness of
detail.   (2) The decidedly Praxitelean character of the full-length
figures of deities on the reverses.   The figures of Herakles (pl. ii. 9,
iii. 3), of Zeus (iv. 4, vii. 2), of Poseidon (v. 1), of Apollo (v. 4,
ix. 10), are all in their attitudes characteristic of the school of
Praxiteles.   The types of Greek deities which we find are sometimes
more distinctive than the style in which they are rendered.   Thus,
on coins of Demetrius, Artemis is sometimes radiate (pl. iii. 1), on
coins of Agathocles (iv. 4) Zeus bears in his hand the three-headed
Hekate, Herakles crowns himself with a wreath, Pallas appears in
short skirts, and many other such strange forms of Greek deities
appear.

   To search out the reasons of these variations of type, reasons to
be found probably in many instances in the influence of local Indian
or Persian legend or belief, would be a very attractive task, and not
hopeless, considering the data furnished us by the legends of the
gold Indo-Scythic coins, as to which we shall presently have
to speak.

   The earliest of the clearly Indian types to make its appearance is
Semi-Hellenic   a dancing-girl, wearing long hanging earrings and
     types.   oriental trousers, on the money of Pantaleon (iii. 9)
and Agathocles (iv. 9).   As we come to a later period, non-
Hellenic types, or types in which there is a non-Hellenic element,
gradually make their way on the coins.   On coins of Philoxenus
(xiii. 9) and Telephus (xxxii. 7) we find a radiate figure of a sun-god

standing, holding a long sceptre. On those of Amyntas (xiv. 11) and Hermaeus (xv. 8) we find the head of a deity wearing Phrygian cap, whence issue rays. But when we reach the issues of King Maues (pls. xvi., xvii.), we find a wealth of most remarkable and original barbaro-Hellenic figures ; a figure resembling Tyche (xvi. 3), holding in one hand a patera, in the other a wheel, who seems to be the original of the still more outlandish figure of Azes' coins (xviii. 10, 11) ; a radiate Artemis, with veil flying round her head (xvi. 4) ; a draped goddess, bearing a crescent on her head, and standing between two stars ; and several others. Still more original is the type (xvi. 9), where a seated Zeus grasps in his extended hand, not, as usual, a Victory (vii. 9) or a thunderbolt (vii. 5), but a being who seems an impersonation of the thunderbolt, and stands in the midst of it ; as well as the type (xvii. 2) where a nymph, perhaps a Maenad, stands grasping two stems of vine. Maues' successors, Azes and Azilises, use types of the same class. A careful consideration of these facts will convince us that by some means or other Maues and his race secured the services of artists who had been instructed by Greeks, but were not restricted by Greek traditions. In fact, in these coins we have the sole remaining relics of an interesting school of art, one of many which existed in Asia in the first century B.C., and which have passed away almost without leaving any memorial. It would further seem that kings, who were the patrons of art, and understood the Greek language, must have been considerably softened and refined by contact with civilized neighbours.

The first of Indian deities to claim a place on the coins is Siva, **Hindu types.** who seems to make his appearance on the coins of Gondophares (pl. xxii. 8, 9), though it must be confessed that this figure may with equal plausibility be called a Poseidon, for the characteristic marks of Siva are absent. But on coins of Kadphises II. the bull, which appears beside the deity, sufficiently proves him to be Ṣiva; and on the money of Kanerkes and his successor he appears in more and more native form, four-armed, and bearing the numerous symbols associated with him in local belief. It is probable that the goddess who appears on the coins of Azes as standing on a lotus, and holding a flower (xix. 5), is either Pārvatī, the dread wife of Ṣiva, or Lakshmī, the goddess of fortune: the supposed lion, which seems on the coin to lie under her left elbow, may be after all only a lump of oxide. These, and the dancer on the coins of Pantaleon and Agathocles, are the only strictly Hindu types to be found on coins before the time of the great Yueh-chi dynasty, when other deities come in, as will be seen by the list given below.

To speak of Parthian types on coins at all may seem a misnomer, **Parthian types.** since there are no original Parthian types in ex-istence, if we except representations of the king himself: in these matters the Parthians were imitators of the Greeks. But there are, notwithstanding, certain types of deities, and a certain style of art, which we learn to associate with the coins of Parthia; and when we can trace these on coins issued in India, a presumption arises that the king who issued them was of Parthian stock. For example, the portraits of Parthian kings, bearded, and wearing the diadema, have quite a distinct aspect; and we find this aspect in the portraits of Gondophares, Pacores, Orthagnes, and Sanabares. The type which represents a City crowning the king, which occurs on the money of Phraates IV. and subsequent kings of Parthia, is used by Zeionises (pl. xxiii. 4); and Nike, who is continually present on Parthian coins, is quite a feature also on our pl. xxiii., which contains coins of the kings of this group. Indeed, some of their coins, such as xxiii. 10 and 11, are altogether of Parthian type.

In view of their types, the gold coins of the conquering Yueh-chi

Types on gold of Yueh-chi. kings are of surpassing interest. The obverse presents us with a figure of the king clad in helmet and armour, which are closely like those borne by the first Arsaces of Parthia on his coins. The reverses are extremely varied, and present us with a multitude of types borrowed from several different mythologies. Had these coins been anepigraphous, their interpretation would have baffled all ingenuity; but fortunately the names of the various deities represented are written beside them in Greek characters, only somewhat disguised by being crushed into Scythian forms. On these types two important papers have been published, one by Mr. Thomas* and one by Dr. Hoffmann.† Though the present writer does not pretend to the linguistic knowledge of either of these scholars, he ventures to discuss their results from the numismatic point of view and that of comparative archaeology.

On these gold coins the following types appear:—

(a.) GREEK AND SEMI-GREEK DEITIES.

Inscriptions.   *Types.*

HΛIOC   Radiate sun-god, holds sceptre.

CAΛHNH   Male moon-deity, holds sceptre.

NANAIA   Female deity holding sceptre, which ends in the fore-part of a horse.

These types occur in the series of coins issued by king Kanerkes with Greek legends only. The names of the deities are given in Greek, not Scythic. Nevertheless, in the types there are clear signs of barbarism. The figure of Helios is identical with that on bilingual coins inscribed with the name of

* *Jainism, or the Early Faith of Asoka; J. R. A. S.* 1877.
† *Abhandlungen f. d. Kunde des Morgenlandes,* vol. vii. (1881), no. 3, p. 139 sqq.

Mioro, and the figure of Nanaia with that on the coins inscribed **NANA**; while the type of 'Salene' is borrowed from the coins inscribed **MAO**, and is male instead of female. Nanaia, though a deity of Persian origin,* was clearly regarded by the die-cutter as Greek, perhaps as identical with Artemis, but there is much that is oriental in her figure.

NANA,
NANA PAO
[OΔIIO]

Female deity holding sceptre, as above; over her forehead, crescent.

The **PAO** is evidently only a suffix. The crescent of course indicates a lunar deity. **NANO** and **OKPO** are combined on a coin published by Prokesch-Osten. *Arch. Zeit.* 1849, pl. x. 8.

HPAKIΛO

Herakles; holds club and apple.

HPO

Artemis clad in long chiton; holds bow and arrow.

The type is unmistakeable, but the legend is puzzling. Mr. Thomas reads it **ZEPO** 'Ceres' (?), but that brings us no nearer to Artemis. I venture to suggest that the word **MEIPO** (see p. lxiii) is intended, for we find in other instances that inappropriate legend sometimes accompanying types which were, as we may conjecture, unintelligible to the die-cutter.

PAO PHOPO

War-god, standing; holds spear and shield.

The word **PAO**, evidently meaning king or royal, may be detached from the legend. The remainder, **PHOPO**, cannot be with certainty explained, but it seems most likely that it is a mere twisting of the Greek **APHΣ**, and that the intention is to portray the Greek war-god. The type suits Ares perfectly.

---

* A long dissertation on her by Hoffmann, l. c., p. 130.

Inscriptions.	*Types.*

PIOM   Pallas, or Roma; holds spear and shield.

Mr. Thomas reads **PIAH**, 'Rhea' (?). But **PIOM**, or even **PⲰM**, is nearer to the actual legend, and the types of Pallas and Roma can scarcely be distinguished; I am therefore inclined to find here an impersonation of the great city, such impersonation being usual in contemporary Roman coins.

CAPAⲠO   Sarapis, holds sceptre; modius on head.

ⲰPON   Deity, wearing modius, holds sceptre.

[ⲰPOH ?]   I am disposed to identify this figure with the Greek Uranus, though he may almost as well stand for the Indian Varuna.

(β.) PERSIAN DEITIES.

AⲐPO,   Fire-god, holding hammer and tongs.

AⲐOPO   Male figure, holding wreath and tongs.

This is the Iranian fire-god, called by Mr. Thomas Atars; but his form is copied from that of the Greek Hephaestus.

APAEIXPO   Sun-god, with hand raised.   (Persian ?)

The origin of the name is obscure: it may even be a mere corruption of **APΔOXPO**.

ΛPOOACΓO   Male deity, holding wreath, horse beside him.

The first letter has usually been corrected to **A**. Hoffmann, however, observes that as it stands the name is near to the Persian word Luhrasp. It is not certain that we have here a sun-god, the horse, his only marked attribute, being not necessarily solar.

MANAO-   Moon-god, four-armed, seated on throne.

BAΓO

Inscriptions.	Types.

Mr. Thomas interprets the legend 'Mâonh Bago,' a particular form of the Iranian moon-deity. Hoffmann recognizes the deity as Bahman (Manō Vohū).

MAO

Moon-god, holds sceptre, wreath, ankus, &c.

Mao is a Zend name for the moon-god.

MIIPO,
MEIPO,
MIOPO,
[ONIO]

Radiate sun-god, holds sceptre, wreath, &c.

[In one case the inscription accompanies a figure of Nanaia.]

The form **MIΘPO** does not, so far as I know, occur. The deity intended seems therefore rather to be the Iranian sun-god Mihira, than his Graeco-Roman counterpart Mithras.

NANA

See above, under Greek deities.

OANINΔA

Victory, holding wreath and sceptre.

The Zend word *Vanaṅt* stands for the star of victory (Hoffmann). Mr. Thomas considers the legend to refer to Anandates, a Persian deity mentioned by Strabo.* But he was a male deity, and of his character we know nothing.

OAΔO

Wind-god running.

"Zend, 'wind-god,' *vātō*" (Hoffmann). The type is very characteristic, and decidedly original.

OPΛAΓNO

War-god; holds spear and sword.

The legend has been read **OPΔAΓNO**, and supposed by Mr. Thomas to refer to Agni. Hoffmann considers the deity to be the Persian war-god Varhran, or Bahram.

ΦAPPO

Deity holding fire, sceptre, sword, &c., some-

---

* Ὠμανοῦ καὶ Ἀναδάτου, Περσικῶν δαιμόνων, page 512 (c).

times wears winged helmet, or stands on a fire; sometimes holds the caduceus of Hermes, and even his purse.

The Persian word *far* or *farr* signifies fire, and that the deity is a fire-god is evident. Hoffmann calls him the god of victory, *ḥvarenaṅh,* " Hoheits und Sieges-glanz."

(γ.) INDIAN DEITIES.

APΔOXPO
[ΔOXPO]

Female deity, holding a cornucopiae.

The type is nearer to that of the Greek Tyche than to any other figure. The legend has been regarded as a transcription of Ardha-ugra, half or consort of Śiva, Pārvatī. And that **OKPO** stands for Śiva is certain, as we shall presently see: but there still remains for explanation the aspirate **X** for **K,** as well as the curious circumstance that the cruel and relentless Pārvatī should appear in so mild and propitious a form. Hoffmann considers the deity intended to be the Persian Ashis, daughter of Ahuro, goddess of fortune. Others suppose her to be Lakshmī, the Indian goddess of fortune, who closely corresponds to Tyche.

MAACHNO

War-god Skanda, holding standard and sword.

There can be little doubt that the legend represents the Sanskrit Mahāsena, ' ruler of a great army,' an epithet of both Śiva and Skanda. The

Inscriptions.   *Types.*

figure so nearly resembles that of Skanda in the present series, that it is safe to identify it with him. Later, Mahāsena reappears, in somewhat different form.

OKPO

Śiva, standing with trident and bull; his hair in form of a shell.

Śiva having four hands, in which he holds a vase, an Indian thunderbolt,* a trident, and a goat: sometimes a wreath or a Greek thunderbolt : he is sometimes phallic.

There has been a quite unnecessary doubt as to the identification of this figure; Hoffmann calls it Ahuro, and von Sallet " Pantheon aus Zeus, Poseidon, Herakles," &c. No doubt there is a Greek element in the type, but the attributes prove beyond any doubt that Śiva (Ugra) is intended. The thunderbolt, trident, and goat, are all attributes of that deity as he appears in Hindu pictures, and the special arrangement of the hair and the phallic nature also belong to him especially. On some of the late coins Śiva has three faces.

CKANΔO
KOMAPO,
BIZAΓO

Two figures of armed deities; one holds standard and sword, one sword and spear.

These figures also can be unhesitatingly identified as Skanda, the Hindu god of war, who bears the epithet of Kumāra, the prince, and Viṣākha, who is called in the Mahābhārata† a son and impersonation of Skanda.

---

* On p. 132 this attribute has been called a drum. Its form is that of a drum, but the occurrence of the Greek thunderbolt in the hand of Siva shows that it is the Indian counterpart of that weapon.

† i. 2588, iii. 14384, &c.

h

Inscriptions.	*Types.*
CKANΔO KOMAPO, MAACHNO, BIZAΓO	Two figures, as before; between them a deity, who is apparently horned. In this remarkable group we find again Skanda Kumāra, and Viṣākha: the third figure appears to be Mahāsena, who is here differentiated from Śiva.
ѠPON	See above, under ' Greek Deities.'

(δ) *Buddha.*

BOΔΔO, OΔYO BOY ⎫ CAKAMA, ⎬]ΓO BOYΔΔO ⎭	Figure of Buddha, standing, preaching. Buddha seated cross-legged (Pl. xxxii. 14).

These coins are most interesting as giving us the earliest known artistic representation of Buddha. The second and longer legend seems to be a transcript of Advaya Buddha Śākyamuni.* On a British Museum specimen **CAKAMA** is clear; the old reading **CAMANA**, with its interpretation Śramana, must therefore be given up.

Style of types. The style in which these various figures are represented is remarkable, and points clearly to a local school. There are a few set schemes according to which all the figures are arranged. Nanaia (xxvi. 10) is in exactly the same attitude as Ardochro (xxvi. 6). The sun-god (xxvii. 9) finds his close parallel in the moon-god (xxvii. 22). Pallas, or Roma (xxviii.40) differs from Ares (xxviii. 17) only in the length of her chiton. This being the case, it is evidently futile to seek the originals of the types of these coins, as one might be tempted to do, on the Roman aurei of the Cæsars. Thus the Roma (xxviii. 20) is closely like Pallas on an aureus of Galba, and the Victory (xxviii. 13) nearly resembles

---

* The word advaya is due to a suggestion of Mr. Bendall ; the full form would be advaya-vādin, ' he who speaks of the one (knowledge).'

Victory on an aureus of Otho; yet we have no right in these and similar cases to assume that the Roman coin is the prototype, and the Indian coin the copy. Rather both coin-types are copies of a conventional and widely current mode of representing the deities. Within the limits set by their conventional notions as to attitudes and drapery the artists employed by the Scythic kings move freely; they vary attributes continually, and in the case of Siva even develop a type quite different from anything to which they can have been accustomed in a Greek school.

V. WEIGHTS.

It is maintained by Gen. Cunningham that the earliest Greek

The purāṇa. coins of India, those of Sophytes, are struck not on the Attic standard, but on a native standard which is based on the rati or grain of *abrus precatorius*. Of these grains, 32 weigh, according to Cunningham, $58\frac{1}{3}$ English gr., according to Thomas 56 gr. We thus reach a unit, the purāṇa, followed in the early punched silver coins of India; and that the money of Sophytes follows the same standard is likely enough, though if so it is rather over-weight.

Apart from these specimens, all the earlier coins of the kings of

Use of Attic standard. Greek descent which were issued in India and to the north of the Caucasus, are struck on the Attic standard (drachm, 67·5 grains) which Alexander made universal in the regions which he conquered, and which was maintained by the Seleucid kings who succeeded him in Asia.

The earliest monarch to strike on another standard is Eucratides; and in the reigns of his successors, Heliocles and Antialcidas, the Attic standard is gradually given up, the new standard advancing in conjunction with the custom of using on the coins Indian transcripts of the Greek legends.

This new standard appears to be identical with that called by
metrologists the Persian, the standard on which
Persian standard. coins were struck in all parts of the Persian Empire,
notably the sigli stamped with the figure of the Persian king, which
must have freely circulated in the northern parts of India, which
paid tribute to the Persians. The standard used by the Indians for
the silver coins, which they issued before the Greek conquest, is as
we have already remarked different. The present standard therefore
would seem not to be native to India, but an importation from
Persia.

In the Persian standard the unit or drachm weighs 84-86 grains:
if therefore the lower standard of the Greek kings of India be
Persian, we must call the heavier pieces, which weigh as a maximum
160 grains, didrachms; and the smaller pieces, which weigh up to 40
grains, hemidrachms. Hitherto the larger pieces have usually been
treated as didrachms, and the smaller as hemidrachms, of Attic
standard, which is clearly wrong. But Sallet also appears to be
wrong in supposing that the larger pieces are tetradrachms, and the
smaller drachms of a standard reduced from the Attic. For the
change from the Attic standard to that which I call the Persian takes
place suddenly, and is evidently due not to any sinking of standard,
but to the adoption for purposes of convenience of a different weight
for coins.

All gold coins before the Indo-Scythic period follow the Attic
standard, somewhat debased. The Indo-Scythic
Gold standard. gold money, as we have already observed, p. liii,
follows the standard of the aurei of Rome.

The following table gives approximately the normal or standard
weights of coins in the various metals issued in India by Greek and
Scythic kings.

PERCY GARDNER.

NORMAL WEIGHTS OF COINS.

GOLD.

	Grains.	Grammes.
Stater of Attic Standard	132·	8·55
Drachm of Attic Standard	66·	4·27
Indo-Scythic distater	248·	16·07
„ stater	124·	8·03
„ quarter-stater . . .	31·	2·01

SILVER.

Tetradrachm of Attic Standard . . .	264·	17·10
Drachm of Attic Standard	66·	4·27
Hemidrachm of Attic Standard . . .	33·	2·13
Obol of Attic Standard	11·	·71
Didrachm of Persian Standard . . .	160·	10·36
Hemidrachm of Persian Standard . . .	40·	2·59
Drachm of Indian Standard . . .	58·	3·75

NICKEL.

Didrachm of Attic Standard . . .	132·?	8·55
Drachm of Attic Standard	66·	4·27

THE ARIAN PALI ALPHABET, ON COINS.

Value.	Forms.	Value.	Forms.	Value.	Forms.
a	1 2 3*	gaṃ		ṭhe	
aṃ	1 2 †	gu	1 2	§ḍa	
‡ā (medial) or ṃ		go		dha	
i		gha		ta	1 2 3
iṃ		cha	1 2	ti	1 2
u		chha	1 2	te	
e		ja	1 2 3	tra	1 2
o		ji	1 2	tṣa	
ka		ju		tsa	
ki		jña		tha	
ku		jha		§da	1 2 3 4 5
ke		jhaṃ		di	1 2 3
kra		jho		du	
kri		ña	1 2	de	1 2
kre	1 2	ṭa		do	
kha	1 2	ṭha		dra	
khu		thi		dha	
khsa		thu		dhra	
ga	1 2 3			§na	1 2 3

* Bottom strokes occur in the case of many letters, such as *a, ga, ja, na,* and *da;* it is therefore sometimes impossible to say whether a letter is intended to be followed by *u* or *r,* or to be only casually varied.

† Forms in square brackets are not found on coins in the British Museum, but are cited as occurring elsewhere on the authority of General Cunningham.

‡ In the Journal Asiatique (xv. 308) M. Senart maintains that this sign has no phonetic value; General Cunningham, with hesitation, assigns to it the value of *a* long: *aṃ* seems on the coins to be sometimes undistinguishable from *ā* and sometimes from *u.*

§ I cannot distinguish on the coins between *na* and *ṇa, da* and *ḍa;* the forms of *da,* ⅃ and 𝔏, are used interchangeably on the coins of Menander.

Value.	Forms.	Value.	Forms.	Value.	Forms.
ni	1 2	mo		vri	
pa	1 2	ya		ṣa	
pi	1 2	yi		ṣi	
pu		yu		ṣva	
pra		ye		sha	
pri		ra		shka	[ ]
pha	1 2	raṃ		shni	[ ]
phi		ri		sa	1 2 3
phre		ru		saṃ	
phsa		rkhe		si	
ba		rte		su	
bi		rma		so	1 2
bu	1 2	rva		sta	
bra		rṣa	[ ]	sti	
bha		la		stra	
bhra	1 2	li		spa	
ma	1 2 3	lu		ha	1 2
mā		lo	1 2	hi	
maṃ		va		hu	
mi		vi		he	
me		vu		ho	

TABLE OF TRANSLITERATIONS AND REN-
DERINGS OF PRAKRIT LEGENDS.

Indian.	Greek equivalent.	English rendering.
	INDIAN PALI.	
Akathukleyasa	ΑΓΑΘΟΚΛΕΟΥΣ	
Paṃtalevasa	ΠΑΝΤΑΛΕΟΝΤΟΣ	
Rajine	ΒΑΣΙΛΕΩΣ	King (*genitive*).
	ARIAN PALI.	
Akathukreyasa*	ΑΓΑΘΟΚΛΕΟΥΣ	
Amitasa	ΑΜΥΝΤΟΥ	
Aṃtialikidasa	ΑΝΤΙΑΛΚΙΔΟΥ	
Aṃtimakhasa	ΑΝΤΙΜΑΧΟΥ	
Apadihatasa	ΑΝΙΚΗΤΟΥ	Invincible (*gen.*).
Apaladatasa	ΑΠΟΛΛΟΔΟΤΟΥ	
Aparajitasa	ΑΝΙΚΗΤΟΥ	Invincible (*gen.*).
Apratihatasa		Invincible (*gen.*).
Apratihatachakrasa		Invincible with the discus (*gen.*).
Apulaphanasa	ΑΠΟΛΛΟΦΑΝΟΥ *sic*	
Arkhebiyasa	ΑΡΧΕΒΙΟΥ	
Artemidorasa	ΑΡΤΕΜΙΔΩΡΟΥ	
Ashshakasa	ΑΡΣΑΚΟΥ	
Avadagaṣasa	ΑΒΔΑΓΑΣΟΥ	
Ayasa	ΑΖΟΥ	
Ayalishasa *or* Ayilishasa	ΑΖΙΛΙΣΟΥ	

* The distinction between long and short *a* is not preserved in this table, as the two forms seem to be used almost indiscriminately.

Indian.	Greek equivalent.	English rendering.
Bhradaputrasa	ΑΔΕΛΦΙΔΕΩΣ	Brother's son (*gen.*).
Bhrata	ΑΔΕΛΦΟΣ	Brother.
Cha		And (*enclitic*).
Chhatrapasa	ΣΑΤΡΑΠΟΥ	Satrap (*gen.*).
Devatratasa		Protected by the gods (*gen.*).
Dhramaṭhidasa		Steadfast in the law (*gen.*). *See below*, sachadhramaṭhidasa.
Dhramikasa	ΔΙΚΑΙΟΥ	Just (*gen.*), for dharmikasa.
Diyamedasa	ΔΙΟΜΗΔΟΥ	
Dianisiyasa	ΔΙΟΝΥΣΙΟΥ	
Epadrasa	ΕΠΑΝΔΡΟΥ	
Evukratidasa *or* Eukratidasa	ΕΥΚΡΑΤΙΔΟΥ	
Gudapharasa *or* Gadapharasa	ΓΟΝΔΟΦΑΡΟΥ *or* ΥΝΔΟΦΕΡΡΟΥ	
Heliyakreyasa	ΗΛΙΟΚΛΕΟΥΣ	
Heramayasa	ΕΡΜΑΙΟΥ	
Hiduja same		Just to those born on the Indus. Same is Sk. samaḥ (*nom.*). Bendall.
Himakapiṣasa	ΟΟΗΜΟ ΚΑΔΦΙΣΟΥ	
Hipastratasa	ΙΠΠΟΣΤΡΑΤΟΥ	
Jayadharasa	ΝΙΚΗΦΟΡΟΥ	Victorious (*gen.*).
Jayaṃtasa *or* Jayatasa		Conquering: a secondary formation from the participle, common in all Prakrits and vernaculars. Bendall.
Jhoilasa	ΖΩΙΛΟΥ	
Jihuniasa	ΖΕΙΩΝΙΣΟΥ	

i

Indian.	Greek equivalent.	English rendering.
Kaliyapaya	ΚΑΛΛΙΟΠΗ	
Kaphsasa	ΚΑΔΑΦΕΣ	
Kariṣiye nagara de-vata		God of the city of Karisi. Cunningham.
Kasasa	ΚΑΔΦΙΣΟΥ	
Kujula or Kuyula	ΚΟΖΟΥΛΟ or ΚΟΖΟΛΑ	
Kushana or Khushana	ΚΟΡΟΝ or ΧΟΡΑΝ	Kushan (tribe).
Lisiasa or Lisikasa	ΛΥΣΙΟΥ	
Mahachhatrapasa		Satrap (gen.).
Maharajasa	ΒΑΣΙΛΕΩΣ	King (gen.).
Maharajabhrata or Maharajabhraha	ΒΑΣΙΛΕΩΣ ΑΔΕΛΦΟΣ	Brother of the king.
Mahatasa or Mahatakasa	ΜΕΓΑΛΟΥ	Great (gen.): Pali, mahanta.
Mahiṣvarasa		Great prince (gen.).
Menadrasa	ΜΕΝΑΝΔΡΟΥ	
Moasa	ΜΑΥΟΥ	
Nikiasa	ΝΙΚΙΟΥ	
Pakurasa	ΠΑΚΟΡΟΥ	
Palanakramasa	ΕΥΕΡΓΕΤΟΥ	Perhaps for Sk. pālanaksha-masa, 'able to protect' (gen.). Ksh not being a Prakrit combination of letters, we have not been able to find an example of it in Arian Pali. Bendall.
Philasinasa or Philusinasa	ΦΙΛΟΞΕΝΟΥ	
Pratichhasa	ΕΠΙΦΑΝΟΥΣ	Illustrious : — for pratīkshiyasa (gen.). Bendall.
Putrasa	ΥΙΟΥ	Son (gen.).

Indian.	Greek equivalent.	English rendering.
Rajabalasa, Ramja-bulasa, &c. }	ΡΑΙΥ	
Rajadirajasa *or* Rajarajasa	ΒΑΣΙΛΕΩΣ } ΒΑΣΙΛΕΩΝ }	King of kings (*gen.*).
Sachadhramathidasa		Steadfast in true law:—for satya-dharmasthitasya (*gen.*). Bendall.
Sagaba		Brother : — for sagarbha. Cunningham.
Sampriyapita		To whom his father is very dear. This seems to be a rendering of the Greek φιλοπάτωρ. Cunningham.
Sarvaloga iṣvarasa		Prince of all the world (*gen.*).
Sasasa		
Spalagadamasa		
Spalahorasa		
Spaliriṣasa	ΣΠΑΛΙΡΙΣΟΥ	
Straṭasa	ΣΤΡΑΤΩΝΟΣ	
Strategasa		General (*gen.*), Greek στρατηγός.
Teliphasa	ΤΗΛΕΦΟΥ	
Ṭheuphilasa	ΘΕΟΦΙΛΟΥ	
Tradatasa	ΣΩΤΗΡΟΣ	Saviour :—perhaps for a Prakrit trāṇadatasa (*gen.*), cf. Sk. trā-ṇakartṛi. Bendall.
Vrishabha	ΤΑΥΡΟΣ	Bull.
Yavugasa *or* Yauasa	ΖΑΟΟΥ	Yueh ? (*gen.*).

CORRIGENDA.

Page 68, no. 4, & p. 69, nos. 9, 10—The object described in the text as a whip over the king's shoulder seems to be merely the falling ends of the regal diadema, greatly exaggerated. On the coins of Azes and succeeding kings this view is adopted.

Pp. 103, 105—The first letter in the name of Gondophares (𝔖) is transliterated sometimes as *ga* and sometimes as *gu*. It may stand for either, or even *gaṃ*

GREEK AND SCYTHIC
KINGS OF BACTRIA AND INDIA.

No.	Wt.	Metal. Size.	Obverse.	Reverse.
			ANDRAGORAS, KING OF PARTHIA? B.C. *cir.* 300. *Gold.*	
			Bust of Zeus r., wearing taenia ; drapery round neck.	ΑΝΔΡΑΓΟΡ[ΟΥ Warrior r., in quadriga driven by Nike, and drawn by four horned horses, galloping.
1	131·9	N ·7	behind, ϺΡ.	[Pl. I. 1.]
				Silver.
			Head of a City r., wearing turreted crown.	ΑΝΔΡΑΓΟΡΟΥ Pallas standing l., clad in chiton and peplos ; holds owl in r., l. rests on shield which is adorned with Gorgon's head ; behind her, spear.
2	255·8	Æ 1·15	behind, ϺΡ.	[Pl. I. 2.]

B

No.	Wt.	Metal. Size.	Obverse.	Reverse.
			### SOPHYTES, KING IN INDIA. *B.C. cir.* 300. *Silver.* Head of the king r., in close-fitting helmet, bound with wreath; wing on cheek-piece.	ΣΩΦΥΤΟΥ Cock r.; above, caduceus.
1	58·3	Æ ·6	on section of neck, **M**.	[Pl. i. 3.]

No.	Wt.	Metal. Size.	Obverse.	Reverse.
				DIODOTUS I., KING OF BACTRIA.
				Revolted *cir.* B.C. 250.
				(*a*) *Gold.*
			Head of the king r., diad.	**ΒΑΣΙΛΕΩΣ** Zeus striding to l., **ΔΙΟΔΟΤΟΥ** hurling thunderbolt; aegis on l. arm; at his feet, eagle l.
1	130·3	Aʹ ·75		to l., wreath. [Pl. i. 4.]
2*	128·3	Aʹ ·75		„ „ [Pl. i. 5.]
				(β) *Silver.*
			Head of the king r., diad.	**ΒΑΣΙΛΕΩΣ** Zeus striding to l., **ΔΙΟΔΟΤΟΥ** hurling thunderbolt; aegis on l. arm; at his feet, eagle l.
3	257·1	Æ1·15		to l., wreath. [Pl. i. 6.]
4	255·7	Æ1·05		„ crescent. [Pl. i. 7.]
5	235·2	Æ 1·		„ mon.
6	62·3	Æ ·7		| to l., Μ . [Pl. i. 8.]
				(γ) *Bronze.*
			Head of Zeus r., laur.	**ΒΑ ΣΙΛΕΩΣ** Artemis, clad in **ΔΙΟΔΟΤΟΥ** short chiton, running r.; holds torch in both hands, quiver at shoulder; beside her, hound running r.
7		Æ ·85		[Pl. i. 9.]

* The gold coins bearing an elderly head of Diodotus, and on the reverse the symbols of wreath and spear-head, are regarded as forgeries. They are very common, and all from one die.

No.	Wt.	Metal. Size.	Obverse.	Reverse.
			EUTHYDEMUS I., KING OF BACTRIA. (Successor of Diodotus II., *cir.* B.C. 220.) *(a) Gold.*	
			Head of the king r., diad.	ΒΑΣΙΛΕΩΣ ΕΥΘΥΔΗΜΟΥ Herakles, bearded, naked, seated l. on rock; in r., club, which also rests on rock.
1	129·	N ·75		to l., ⋈. [Pl. I. 10.]
			(β) Silver; middle-aged portrait. Head of the king r., diad.	ΒΑΣΙΛΕΩΣ ΕΥΘΥΔΗΜΟΥ Herakles, bearded, naked, seated l. on rock; in r., club, which also rests on rock.
2	254·6	Æ 1·1		to r., ⋈. [Pl. I. 11.]
3	256·5	Æ 1·		„ „
4	244 2	Æ 1·1		„ „; below, N. [I. O. C.]
5	258·2	Æ 1·		to l., ⋈. [Pl. II. 1.]
6	252·5	Æ 1·15		„ ⋈. [I. O. C. Pl. II. 2.]
7	255·	Æ 1·1		„ „
8	257·7	Æ 1·15		„ „ [Pl. II. 3.]
9	211·2	Æ 1·		(barbarous.)

No.	Wt.	Metal. Size.	Obverse.	Reverse.
			Head of the king r., diad.	**ΒΑΣΙΛΕΩΣ** Herakles, bearded, **ΕΥΘΥΔΗΜΟΥ** naked, seated l. on rock, on which is spread lion's skin; in r. hand, club, which rests on his knee.
10	252·4	Æ 1·15		to r., ℞ . (traces of rock under club.) [Pl. II. 4.]
11	249·	Æ 1·		„ „ (semi-barbarous.)
12	186·5	Æ 1·		„ „ „

(γ) *Silver; elderly portrait.*

No.	Wt.	Metal. Size.	Obverse.	Reverse.
			Head of the king r., diad.	**ΒΑΣΙΛΕΩΣ** Herakles, bearded, **ΕΥΘΥΔΗΜΟΥ** naked, seated l. on rock, on which is spread lion's skin; in r. hand, club, which rests on his knee.
13	256·7	Æ 1·1		to r., ℞ . [Pl. II. 5.]
14	60·8	Æ ·65		to r., ℞ . [Pl. II. 6.]

(δ) *Bronze.*

No.	Wt.	Metal. Size.	Obverse.	Reverse.
			Head of bearded Herakles r., bare.	**ΒΑΣΙΛΕΩΣ** Free horse r., **ΕΥΘΥΔΗΜΟΥ** prancing.
15		Æ ·85		
16		Æ ·85		[I. O. C. Pl. II. 7.]
17		Æ ·85		[I. O. C.]
			Head of Zeus r., laur.	**ΒΑΣΙΛΕΩΣ** Free horse r., **ΕΥΘΥΔΗΜΟΥ** prancing.
18		Æ ·7		to r., ℞ . [I. O. C. Pl. II. 8.]

No.	Wt.	Metal. Size.	Obverse.	Reverse.
			DEMETRIUS, KING OF INDIA.	
			(Son and successor of Euthydemus I.)	
			(a) *Silver.*	
			Bust of the king r., diad., wearing elephant's scalp.	ΒΑΣΙΛΕΩΣ ΔΗΜΗΤΡΙΟΥ Young Herakles, facing; holds in l. hand, club and lion's skin; with r. hand, crowns himself with ivy-wreath.
1	259·5	Æ 1·3		to l., Ρ̣ . [Pl. ii. 9.]
2	260·7	Æ 1·2		„ „ [I. O. C.]
3	263·	Æ 1·35		„ Φ̵ .
4	220·2	Æ 1·15 (plated)		„ „ [I. O. C.]
5	235·5	Æ 1·25		„ Σ; to r., **A**. (semi-barbarous.)
6	61·	Æ ·85		to l., Ρ̣ . [I. O. C. Pl. ii. 10.]
7	55·5	Æ ·8		„ ⋈; to r., ⊘. [I. O. C.]
8	52·8	Æ ·8	(countermark : Σ, and Herakles crowning himself.)	„ Δ. „
9	9·	Æ ·5	(head, not bust.)	to l., Ρ̣ . [Pl. ii. 11.]
10	9·	Æ ·5		„ „
11	10·5	Æ ·5		„ „ [I. O. C. Pl. ii. 12.]
12	10·	Æ ·45		„ Φ̵ .

No.	Wt.	Metal. Size.	Obverse.	Reverse.
				(β) Bronze.
			Bust of Herakles r., bearded, crowned with ivy; lion's skin round neck, club over shoulder.	ΒΑΣΙΛΕΩΣ Artemis, radiate, ΔΗΜΗΤΡΙΟΥ facing, wearing short chiton; holds in l. hand, bow; with r. hand, draws arrow from quiver at her shoulder.
13		Æ 1·		to l., ⚏.
14		Æ 1·		„ „ [I. O. C. Pl. III. 1.]
			Gorgon-head, on round shield.	ΒΑΣΙΛΕΩΣ Trident. ΔΗΜΗΤΡΙΟΥ
15		Æ 1·35		to l., Ⱥ.
			Head of elephant r., bell hung round neck.	ΒΑΣΙΛΕΩΣ Caduceus. ΔΗΜΗΤΡΙΟΥ
16		Æ 1·15		to l., ⟨Φ⟩. [I. O. C. Pl. III. 2.]

No.	Wt.	Metal. Size.	Obverse.	Reverse.

EUTHYDEMUS II., KING OF INDIA.

(Son and successor? of Demetrius.)

(a) *Silver.*

			Bust of the king r., diad.	**ΒΑΣΙΛΕΩΣ** Young Herakles, **ΕΥΘΥΔΗΜΟΥ** facing, ivy-crowned; holds in r. hand, wreath of ivy; in l. hand, club and lion's skin.
1	260·7	Æ1·35		to l., ℞. [Pl. III. 3.]
2	65·1	Æ ·75		to l., ✧
3	63·5 (plated)	Æ ·75		„ „ [Pl. III. 4.]

(β) *Nickel.*

| | | | Head of Apollo r., laur. | **ΒΑΣΙΛΕΩΣ**   Tripod-lebes. **ΕΥΘΥΔΗΜΟΥ** |
| 4 | 118·2 | NI ·95 | | to l., ✧.   [Pl. III. 5.] |

(γ) *Bronze.*

			Head of Apollo r., laur.	**ΒΑΣΙΛΕΩΣ** Tripod-lebes. **ΕΥΘΥΔΗΜΟΥ**
5		Æ 1·1		to l., ✧. [Pl. III. 6.]
			Head of bearded Herakles r., bare.	**ΒΑΣΙΛΕΩΣ** Free horse r., **ΕΥΘΥΔΗΜΟΥ** prancing.
6		Æ ·9		[Pl. III. 7.]

No.	Wt.	Metal. Size.	Obverse.	Reverse.
			### PANTALEON, KING OF INDIA. (Son and successor? of Demetrius.) *(a) Nickel.*	
1	110·2	NI·95	Bust of young Dionysos r., wearing ivy-wreath; thyrsos over shoulder.	ΒΑΣΙΛΕΩΣ Panther to r., ΠΑΝΤΑΛΕΟΝΤΟΣ l. fore-paw raised. to l., **EY**?
			(β) Bronze, round.	
2		Æ ·95	Bust of young Dionysos r., wearing ivy-wreath; thyrsos over shoulder.	ΒΑΣΙΛΕΩΣ Panther to r., ΠΑΝΤΑΛΕΟΝΤΟΣ l. fore-paw raised. to l., **A**. [Pl. iii. 8.]
			(γ) Bronze, square.	
3		Æ ·95	𝌆 𝌆 𝌆 (*Rājine Paṃ-talevasa**). 𝌆𝌆 𝌆𝌆𝌆 Female figure l. with long pendants from her ears, clad in oriental dress with trousers; holds in her r. hand a flower.	ΒΑΣΙΛΕΩΣ Maneless lion r., ΠΑΝΤΑΛΕΟΝΤΟΣ in incuse square. [Pl. iii. 9.]
4		Æ ·85		
5		Æ ·9		[I. O. C.]

* I repeat General Cunningham's reading of this inscription and those on the coins of Agathocles. The Indian inscription in the text is a facsimile taken from the inscriptions on the coins: some of the forms of letters seem abnormal.

c

No.	Wt.	Metal. Size.	Obverse.	Reverse.
			AGATHOCLES, KING OF INDIA.	
			(Son and successor ? of Demetrius.)	
			(α) *Silver; with portraits of his predecessors.*	
			ΑΛΕΞΑΝΔΡΟΥ ΤΟΥ ΦΙΛΙΠΠΟΥ Head of Alexander as Herakles r., in lion's skin.	ΒΑΣΙΛΕΥΟΝΤΟΣ Zeus seated ΑΓΑΘΟΚΛΕΟΥΣ l. on throne ΔΙΚΑΙΟΥ with back; holds eagle and long sceptre.
1	251·2	Æ 1·4		to l., ℞ . [Pl. iv. 1.]
			ΔΙΟΔΟΤΟΥ Head of ΣΩΤΗΡΟΣ Diodotus r., diad.	ΒΑΣΙΛΕΥΟΝΤΟΣ Zeus striding ΑΓΑΘΟΚΛΕΟΥΣ to l., hurling ΔΙΚΑΙΟΥ thunderbolt, aegis on l. arm; at his feet, eagle l.
2	263·5	Æ 1·3		to l., wreath; to r., ⊟. [Pl. iv. 2.]
			ΕΥΘΥΔΗΜΟΥ Head ΘΕΟΥ of Euthydemus I. r., diad.	ΒΑΣΙΛΕΥΟΝΤΟΣ Herakles, ΑΓΑΘΟΚΛΕΟΥΣ bearded, ΔΙΚΑΙΟΥ naked, seated l. on rock; in r. hand, club, which rests on a rock.
3	261·2	Æ 1·2		to r., Φ. [Pl. iv. 3.]
			(β) *Silver; with his own portrait.*	
			Bust of the king r., diad.	ΒΑΣΙΛΕΩΣ Zeus, facing, clad ΑΓΑΘΟΚΛΕΟΥΣ in himation; holds in r. hand, three-headed Hekate who bears two torches; in his l. hand, long sceptre.
4	240·8	Æ 1·2		to l., Φ. [Pl. iv. 4.]
5	63·6	Æ ·8			[Pl. iv. 5.]

No.	Wt.	Metal. Size.	Obverse.	Reverse.
			(γ) *Nickel.*	
			Bust of Dionysos r., wearing ivy-wreath, thyrsos over shoulder.	ΒΑΣΙΛΕΩΣ Panther r., touching a vine with ΑΓΑΘΟΚΛΕΟΥΣ his raised paw.
6	117·5	NI 1·		to l., Φ. [Pl. ɪv. 6.]
7	63·5	NI ·65		| below, K. [Pl. ɪv. 7.]
			(δ) *Bronze, round.*	
			Bust of Dionysos r., wearing ivy-wreath, thyrsos over shoulder.	ΒΑΣΙΛΕΩΣ Panther r., touching a vine with ΑΓΑΘΟΚΛΕΟΥΣ his raised paw.
8		Æ ·9		to l., R. [I. O. C. Pl. ɪv. 8.]
			(ε) *Bronze ; square ; bilingual.*	
			(*Rājine Akathukleyasa*). Female figure l. with long pendants from her ears, clad in oriental drapery with trousers ; holds in her r. hand a flower.	ΒΑΣΙΛΕΩΣ Maneless lion r., ΑΓΑΘΟΚΛΕΟΥΣ in incuse square.
9		Æ ·9		
10		Æ1·05		
11		Æ1·05		
12		Æ 1·		[I. O. C. Pl. ɪv. 9.]
13		Æ ·8		,,
14		Æ ·95		

No.	Wt.	Metal. Size.	Obverse.	Reverse.
			(ζ) *Bronze; square; Indian legend.*	
15		Æ ·75	ⲧ∧ⳅⳁⱨⳁ (*Aka-thukreyasa*). Buddhist stupa, surmounted by star.	ⲱⲧⲩⳋⳍ (*Hiduja Same*). Tree in a square railed enclosure. letters? in field. [Pl. IV. 10.]

ANTIMACHUS, KING OF INDIA.

(Descendant and successor of Diodotus?).

(a) *Silver.*

No.	Wt.	Metal. Size.	Obverse.	Reverse.
			Bust of the king r., diad., wearing causia.	ΒΑΣΙΛΕΩΣ ΘΕΟΥ ΑΝΤΙΜΑΧΟΥ Poseidon, facing, wearing himation and wreath; holds in r. hand, trident; in l., palm, bound with fillet.
1	262·3	Æ1·35		to r., Ⓝ. [Pl. V. 1.]
2	260·5	Æ1·15		„ „
3	252·3	Æ 1·2		„ ℞.
4	59·	Æ ·8		to r., Ⓝ.
5	31·5	Æ ·6		to r., ⋈. [Pl. V. 2.]
6	10·6	Æ ·45		to r., ℞. [I. O. C. Pl. V. 3.]

No.	Wt.	Metal. Size.	Obverse.	Reverse.
				EUCRATIDES, KING OF BACTRIA AND INDIA. (Contemporary of Antiochus IV. and Demetrius I. of Syria.) (a) *Silver ; type, Apollo.*
			Bust of the king r., diad.: fillet-border.	ΒΑΣΙΛΕΩΣ Apollo l., clad in ΕΥΚΡΑΤΙΔΟΥ chlamys and boots; holds arrow and bow.
1	257·2	Æ 1·2		to l., ⋈.
2	256·5	Æ 1·3		„ ⋈.
3	261·	Æ 1·3		„ „ [I. O. C. Pl. v. 4.]
4	261·	Æ 1·3		„ „ [I. O. C.]
5	58·5	Æ ·7	(border of dots.)		to l., **ΚΙ**. [I. O. C. Pl. v. 5.]
				(β) *Silver ; type, The Dioscuri.*
			Bust of the king r., diad.: fillet-border.	ΒΑΣΙΛΕΩΣ The Dioscuri ΕΥΚΡΑΤΙΔΟΥ charging r., holding long lances and palms.
6	258·5	Æ1·25		below, ℞. [Pl. v. 6.]
7	259·	Æ1·25		„ ⋈. [I. O. C.]

No.	Wt.	Metal. Size.	Obverse.	Reverse.
			Bust of the king r., diad., and wearing helmet in the shape of a causia, adorned with ear and horn of bull, and crest : fillet-border.	ΒΑΣΙΛΕΩΣ ΜΕΓΑΛΟΥ ΕΥΚΡΑΤΙΔΟΥ The Dioscuri charging r., holding long lances and palms.
8	261·2	Æ1·35		below Φ.
9	258·2	Æ1·35		„ 回. [Pl. v. 7.]
10	259·6	Æ 1·3		„ ⋀⋀.
11	258·8	Æ 1·2		„ ⋈.
12	258·7	Æ1·35		„ „
13	258·2	Æ 1·3		„ ⋈. [Pl. v. 8.]
14	244·5	Æ1·35		to l., ⊕. [I. O. C.]
15	57·5	Æ ·8		below, Φ. [Pl. v. 9.]
16	62·3	Æ ·75	(border of dots.)	„ „
17	59·5	Æ ·75	(„)	„ N. (semi-barbarous.)
18	55·3	Æ ·75	(„)	to l., ⋈. (ΒΑΣΙΛΕΩΣ written ΣΙΛΕΩΣ). [I. O. C.]

No.	Wt.	Metal. Size.	Obverse.	Reverse.
				(γ) *Silver ; type, Pilei of Dioscuri.*
			Bust of the king r., diad.	ΒΑΣΙΛΕΩΣ　The pilei of the ΕΥΚΡΑΤΙΔΟΥ　Dioscuri, laur., surmounted by stars ; and two palms.
19	9·9	Æ ·45		below, ℞.　　[I. O. C.]
20	9·1	Æ ·45		„ 𝄪.
21	9·9	Æ ·45		„ ⱖ.
22	10·8	Æ ·5		„ ⱖ.　[I. O. C.　Pl. v. 10.]
23	9·5	Æ ·45		„ „　　[I. O. C.]
24	10·	Æ ·45		„ Κ.
25	9·2	Æ ·45		„ Ⱳ.
26	7·3 (broken)	Æ ·4		„ ⱨ.　　[I. O. C.]
			Bust of the king r., diad. and helmeted.	ΒΑΣΙΛΕΩΣ　Similar type. ΕΥΚΡΑΤΙΔΟΥ
27	9·9	Æ ·45		below, Ⱳ.
28	10·1	Æ ·45		„ „　　[Pl. v. 11.]
29	10·	Æ ·45		„ „
30	6· (broken)	Æ ·4		„ ΠΓ.　　[I. O. C.]

No.	Wt.	Metal. Size.	Obverse.	Reverse.
			(δ) *Bronze; round; type, Dioscuri.*	
			Bust of the king r., diad. and helmeted: fillet-border.	ΒΑΣΙΛΕΩΣ ΜΕΓΑΛΟΥ ΕΥΚΡΑΤΙΔΟΥ The Dioscuri charging r., holding long lances and palms.
31	Æ ·95			below, ⋈.
32	Æ 1·05			„ „
33	Æ ·9			„ ⩎. [I. O. C.]
34	Æ ·8			„ ⊠. [I. O. C. Pl. vi. 1.]
			Similar.	Same inscr. One of the Dioscuri charging r., holding long lance.
35	Æ ·6			[Pl. vi. 2.]
			(ε) *Bronze; square; type, Dioscuri.*	
			ΒΑΣΙΛΕΩΣ ΜΕΓΑ-ΛΟΥ ΕΥΚΡΑΤΙΔΟΥ Bust of the king r., diad. and helmeted.	𐨿𐨸𐨪.∼ᵕ (*Māhārajasa Evu-krātidasa* or *Eü-krātidasa*). The Dioscuri charging r., holding long lances and palms.
36	Æ ·85			to l., ⧈ ; to r., **E**. [I. O. C. Pl. vi. 3.]
37	Æ ·75			„ „ „ „ [I. O. C.]
38	Æ ·9			„ „ „ „
39	Æ ·8			„ ⊕.

No.	Wt.	Metal. Size.	Obverse.	Reverse.
			ΒΑΣΙΛΕΩΣ ΜΕΓΑ-ΛΟΥ ΕΥΚΡΑΤΙΔΟΥ Bust of the king r., diad. and helmeted.	𐨤𐨩𐨪.~𐨁 (*Māhārajasa Evu-krātidasa* or *Eü-krātidasa*). The Dioscuri charging r., holding long lances and palms.
40	Æ ·95			to r., ⊕.
41	Æ ·9			„ ⊟.
42	Æ ·9			„ ⊟.
43	Æ ·95			„ „
44	Æ ·85			„ ⊞.
45	Æ ·85			„ ⊠. [I. O. C.]
46	Æ ·85			„ ⊢P. „
47	Æ ·9			„ △.
48	Æ ·9			„ ⌐R.
49	Æ ·85			„ ⊼.
50	Æ ·8			„ PⅠ. (𝟸 for 𝟽).
51	Æ ·9			„ ⊡. [I. O. C.]
52	Æ ·9			„
53	Æ ·7			to r., ⊼. [I. O. C.]
54	Æ ·65			„ ⊞.
55	Æ ·7			[I. O. C. Pl. vi. 4.]

D

No.	Wt.	Metal. Size.	Obverse.	Reverse.
			ΒΑΣΙΛΕΩΣ ΜΕΓΑ-ΛΟΥ ΕΥΚΡΑΤΙΔΟΥ Head of the king r., diad., without helmet.	ᐱᎽꓶ∼ᵕ (*Māharajasa Evu-* ᛐᏋᏇ·ᕁᏠᏋ *krātidasa*). The pilei of the Dioscuri surmounted by stars, and two palms.
56		Æ ·6		
57		Æ ·6		[I. O. C. Pl. vɪ. 5.]
			(ζ) *Bronze; square; type, Nike.*	
			ΒΑΣΙΛΕΩΣ ΜΕΓΑ-ΛΟΥ ΕΥΚΡΑΤΙΔΟΥ Bust of the king r., diad. and helmeted.	ᐱᎽꓶ∼ᵕ (*Māharajasa Evu-* ᏇᏋᏇᏠᏋ *kratidasa*). Nike l., bearing wreath and palm.
58		Æ ·65		to l., ⊕.
59		Æ ·75		„ „ [I. O. C. Pl. vɪ. 6.]
60		Æ ·7		„ „
61		Æ ·65	Similar? (obscure coin).	Same inscr.? Nike r., bearing wreath and palm.
			ΜΕΓΑΛΟΥ ΒΑΣΙΛ-ΕΩΣ ΕΥΚΡΑΤΙΔΟΥ Bust of the king l., helmeted, striking with spear.	Same inscr. Nike r., bearing wreath and palm.
62		Æ ·9		to r., ⊠. [I. O. C. Pl. vɪ. 7.]

No.	Wt.	Metal. Size.	Obverse.	Reverse.
			(η) Bronze; square; type, Zeus.	
			ΒΑΣΙΛΕΩΣ ΜΕΓΑ-ΛΟΥ ΕΥΚΡΑΤΙΔΟΥ Bust of the king r., diad. and helmeted.	ꓕꓒꓵꓶꓕꓜꓢꓥꓵꓕꓴꓶ (*Karisiye nagara devata?**). Zeus seated l. on throne; holds wreath and palm; in front, forepart of elephant r.; behind, conical object.
63		Æ ·7		to r., ⚆. [Pl. vi. 8.]
			EUCRATIDES, WITH HELIOCLES AND LAODICE. (Father and mother of Eucratides.) *Silver.*	
			ΒΑΣΙΛΕΥΣ ΜΕΓΑΣ ΕΥΚΡΑΤΙΔΗΣ Bust of Eucratides r., diad. and helmeted.	ΗΛΙΟΚΛΕΟΥΣ Busts jugate r. ΚΑΙ ΛΑΟΔΙΚΗΣ of Heliocles, with bare head; and Laodice, diad.
1	251·4	Ꭱ 1·25	(fillet-border).	to l., Ш. (fillet-border). [I. O. C. Pl. vi. 9.]
2	61·1	Ꭱ ·8		to l., Ш. [Pl. vi. 10.]

* This is the conjectural reading of Gen. Cunningham, who interprets, 'the god of the city of Karisi.' These coins are sometimes restruck upon money of Apollodotus: it seems, however, not improbable that they may have been issued after the death of Eucratides. *See* Introduction.

No.	Wt.	Metal. Size.	Obverse.	Reverse.
				PLATO. B.C. 166. (Contemporary of Eucratides.) (a) *Silver.*
1	249·	Æ 1·3	Bust of the king r., diad. and wearing helmet adorned with ear and horn of bull, and crest : fillet-border.	ΒΑΣΙΛΕΩΣ ΕΠΙΦΑΝΟΥΣ ΠΛΑΤΩΝΟΣ Helios r., radiate, clad in chiton and chlamys; in quadriga. to r., ℍ; in ex., ΡΜΙ.* [Pl. vi. 11.] (year 147 of the Seleucid era.)

* The Ρ can scarcely be considered a certainty, but a down stroke is visible, which seems to prove that a third letter existed.

No.	Wt.	Metal. Size.	Obverse.	Reverse.

HELIOCLES.

(Son or brother of Eucratides.)

(a) *Silver; Greek inscription; Attic weight.*

No.	Wt.	Metal. Size.	Obverse.	Reverse.
			Bust of the king r., diad.: fillet-border.	ΒΑΣΙΛΕΩΣ ΗΛΙΟΚΛΕΟΥΣ ΔΙΚΑΙΟΥ Zeus, laur., facing, clad in himation; holds winged thunderbolt and long sceptre.
1	261·2	Æ 1·3		to l., ᛕᛈ. [Pl. VII. 1.]
2	258·	Æ 1·25		„ „ [I. O. C.]
3	259·7	Æ 1·25		„ Σ. [Pl. VII. 2.]
4	249·8	Æ 1·15		„ ᛒ.
5	246 6	Æ 1·4		in ex., ΠΓ.
6	240·8	Æ 1·3		to l., ᛖᛜ. [I. O. C.]
7	205·1	Æ 1·05 (plated)		„ ᚱ.
8	58·9	Æ ·8		in ex., ΠΓ. [Pl. VII. 3.]
9	56·7	Æ ·8		„ Δ or Λ.
10	56·8	Æ ·8		to l., ᛒᛁ. (inscr. semi-barbarous.) [I. O. C.]

No.	Wt.	Metal. Size.	Obverse.	Reverse.
			(β) *Barbarous copies in bronze.*	
			Rude copy of bust of Heliocles r., diad.: fillet-border.	Barbarous degradation of— BAΣIΛEΩΣ Zeus, facing; HΛIOKΛEOYΣ holds thunder-ΔIKAIOY bolt and long sceptre.
11		Æ 1·2		
12		Æ 1·1		[I. O. C.]
13		Æ 1·2		[I. O. C.] (restruck on type next described.)
			Similar.	BAΣIΛEΩΣ Horse trotting l. HΛIIΛEYΣ ΔIIAIY (varied).
14		Æ 1·1		
15		Æ 1·1		
16		Æ 1·15		[I. O. C.]
17		Æ 1·1		[I. O. C.]
18		Æ ·75		[Pl. VII. 4.]
19		Æ ·7		
20		Æ ·7		[I. O. C.]
21		Æ ·6		

No.	Wt.	Metal. Size.	Obverse.	Reverse.
				(ANOTHER HELIOCLES ?). (γ) *Silver ; Indian inscription ; Persian weight.* **ΒΑΣΙΛΕΩΣ ΔΙΚΑΙ-ΟΥ ΗΛΙΟΚΛΕΟΥΣ** Bust of the king r., diad..	𐨀𐨿 (*Māhārajasa dhramikasa Heliyakreyasa*). Zeus, laur., facing, clad in himation ; holds winged thunderbolt and long sceptre.
22	146·4	Æ 1·05		to l., ⊕. [I. O. C. Pl. VII. 5.]
23	34·5	Æ ·65		to l., **Σ**. [I. O. C. Pl. VII. 6.]
24	34·2	Æ ·65		,, ,,
25	26·3	Æ ·65		,, 中.
				(δ) *Bronze ; square.* **ΒΑΣΙΛΕΩΣ ΔΙΚΑΙ-ΟΥ ΗΛΙΟΚΛΕΟΥΣ** Bust of the king r., diad.	(*Māhārajasa dhramikasa Heliyakreyasa*). Elephant l.
26		Æ ·85		below, 𐨎.
27		Æ ·85		,, ,,

No.	Wt.	Metal. Size.	Obverse.	Reverse.
			ΒΑΣΙΛΕΩΣ ΔΙΚΑΙ-ΟΥ ΗΛΙΟΚΛΕΟΥΣ Bust of the king r., diad., bearded.	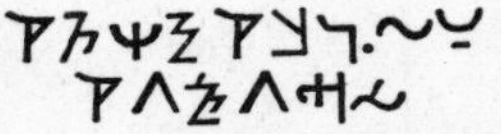 ͳ𐨱ψξ ͳ𐨤𐨮.~ᴗ (*Māhārajasa* ͳ𐨮𐨂𐨣𐨱𐨫 *dhramikasa Heliyakreyasa*). Elephant l.
28		Æ ·8*		below, Σ.
29		Æ ·85		above, 𐨐. (inscr. ends *kre-sa-sa*). [I. O. C. Pl. VII. 7.]
			ΒΑΣΙΛΕΩΣ ΔΙΚΑΙ-ΟΥ ΗΛΙΟΚΛΕΟΥΣ Elephant r.	Same inscr. Indian bull r.
30		Æ ·8		[I. O. C. Pl. VII. 8.]
31		Æ ·95		to l., 𐨀.

* Restruck on a coin of Strato, the characters � remaining on the reverse from previous striking.

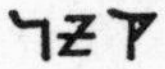

No.	Wt.	Metal. Size.	Obverse.	Reverse.
			ANTIALCIDAS.	
			(a) Silver; Attic weight.	
			Bust of the king r., diad.: fillet-border.	ΒΑΣΙΛΕΩΣ ΝΙΚΗΦΟΡΟΥ ΑΝΤΙΑΛΚΙΔΟΥ Zeus, laur., seated l. on throne; holds in r., Nike, who bears wreath and palm; in l., long sceptre; in field l., forepart of elephant with bell round neck, who raises his trunk.
1	257·2	Æ 1·35		to r.,)Я(. [I. O. C. Pl. vii. 9.]
			(β) Silver; Indian weight.	
			ΒΑΣΙΛΕΩΣ ΝΙΚΗΦΟΡΟΥ ΑΝΤΙΑΛΚΙΔΟΥ Bust of the king r., diad.	𐨤𐨪𐨿𐨜 ... (*Māhā-rajasa jayadharasa Amtialikidasa*). Zeus seated l. on throne; holds in r. hand, palm and wreath; in l., sceptre; to l., small elephant upwards, who grasps the wreath in his trunk.
2	34·5	Æ ·65		to r., ⋈. [Pl. vii. 10]
			Same inscr. Bust of the king r, diad.	Same inscr. Zeus seated l. on throne; holds in r. hand, Nike; in l., sceptre; to l., forepart of elephant, who raises his trunk.
3	36·4	Æ ·65		below throne, ⋈. (elephant r.)
4	38·	Æ ·7		to r., ⋈. „ [I. O. C.]
5	37·9	Æ ·65	(king wears causia).	below throne,)Я(. „ [Pl. vii. 11.]

E

No.	Wt.	Metal. Size.	Obverse.	Reverse.
			ΒΑΣΙΛΕΩΣ ΝΙΚΗ-ΦΟΡΟΥ ΑΝΤΙΑΛ-ΚΙΔΟΥ Bust of the king r., diad.	ᚼᚠᚵᛉ ᚠᚴ ᚽ.~ᛩ (*Māhā-* ᚠᚴᛏᛆᚦᛏᚻ(ᚴ)ᚦ *rajasa jayadharasa Aṃtialikidasa*). Zeus seated l. on throne; holds in r. hand, Nike; in l., sceptre; to l., forepart of elephant, who raises his trunk.
6	33·3	Æ ·65	(king helmeted).	to r., ⟨symbol⟩. (elephant r.)
7	34·5	Æ ·7	,,	below throne, ⟨symbol⟩. ,,
8	37·2	Æ ·65	,,	to r., ⟨symbol⟩. ,, [I. O. C.]
9	35·8	Æ ·65	,,	,, ,, (elephant facing). [Pl. vii. 12.]
10	37·8	Æ ·65	,,	,, ,, (elephant l.) [I. O. C.]
11	37·6	Æ ·65	(king wears causia).	,, ,, ,,
12	37·6	Æ ·7	,,	,, ,, [I. O. C." Pl. vii. 13.]
			Same inscr. Bust of the king r., diad.	Same inscr. Zeus seated l. on throne; holds in r. hand, Nike; in l., sceptre; to l., forepart of elephant l., who carries off the wreath of Nike.
13	36·5	Æ ·6	(king wears causia).	below throne, ⟨symbol⟩.
14	33·9	Æ ·6	,,	,, ,,
15	33·1	Æ ·65		,, ⟨symbol⟩. [Pl. vii. 14.]

No.	Wt.	Metal. Size.	Obverse.	Reverse.
				(γ) *Bronze ; round.*
			ΒΑΣΙΛΕΩΣ ΝΙΚΗ-ΦΟΡΟΥ ΑΝΤΙΑΛ-ΚΙΔΟΥ Bust of Zeus r., with hand hurling thunderbolt.	𐨤𐨪𐨥𐨫𐨩 𐨤𐨩 𐨫.~𐨫 (*Mahā-rajasa jayadharasa Aṃtialikidasa*). Laureate pilei of the Dioscuri, surmounted by stars; between them, two palms.
16		Æ ·9		to r., 𐨪𐨯.
17		Æ ·85		to l., „ [Pl. VIII. 1.]
18		Æ ·85		„ „
				(δ) *Bronze ; square.*
			ΒΑΣΙΛΕΩΣ ΝΙΚΗ-ΦΟΡΟΥ ΑΝΤΙΑΛ-ΚΙΔΟΥ Bust of Zeus r., bare-headed ; thunderbolt over l. shoulder.	𐨤𐨪𐨥𐨫𐨩 𐨤𐨩 𐨫.~𐨫 (*Mahā-rajasa jayadharasa Aṃtialikidasa*). Laureate pilei of the Dioscuri, surmounted by stars; between them, two palms.
19		Æ ·75		to l., Ⱥ; to r., Σ. [Pl. VIII. 2.]
20		Æ ·8		„ Ⱥ; „ „
21		Æ ·75		„ Ⱥ; „ „
22		Æ ·8		„ „ „ „ [I. O. C.]
23		Æ ·7		„ 𐤊
24		Æ ·75		„ „ „
25		Æ ·75		„ „

No.	Wt.	Metal. Size.	Obverse.	Reverse.
			ΒΑΣΙΛΕΩΣ ΝΙΚΗ-ΦΟΡΟΥ ΑΝΤΙΑΛ-ΚΙΔΟΥ Bust of Zeus r., laur., with hand hurling thunderbolt.	ꡖꡗꡓꡋꡗ ꡖꡗꡔ ꡗ.~ꡗ (*Māhā-* ꡖꡗꡤꡜꡗꡖꡗ(ꡜ)ꡗ *rajasa jayadharasa Amtialikidasa*). Laureate pilei of the Dioscuri, surmounted by stars; between them, two palms.
26	Æ ·75			to l., ℞ .
27	Æ ·75			„ „
28	Æ ·7			„ ℞ .
29	Æ ·7			„ „ [Pl. viii. 3.]
30	Æ ·85			above, „
			Same inscr., blundered. Aegis.	Same inscr., blundered. Palm and wreath.
31	Æ ·85			below, ⳩ . [I. O. C. Pl. viii. 4.]

LYSIAS. 29

No.	Wt.	Metal. Size.	Obverse.	Reverse.
				LYSIAS. (a) *Silver.* **ΒΑΣΙΛΕΩΣ ΑΝΙΚΗ-ΤΟΥ ΛΥΣΙΟΥ** Bust of the king r., diad.	𐨤𐨗⁓𐨆𐨱𐨤𐨿𐨗 𐨤𐨩𐨗⁓𐨬 𐨤𐨱𐨫𐨯 (*Māhārajasa apadihātasa Lisikasa*). Young Herakles, facing; holds in l. hand, club, palm, and lion's skin; with r. hand crowns himself with vine-leaves.
1	30·8	Ꭱ ·65		to l., 𐨀; to r., Σ. [Pl. viii. 5.]
2	37·4	Ꭱ ·7	(king wears elephant's scalp).	„ „ „ „ (palm not visible.)
3	37·9	Ꭱ ·7	„ „	„ „ „ „ [I.O.C. Pl. viii. 6.]
4	34·4	Ꭱ ·7	„ „	„)𐨪(. [I. O. C.]
5	36·	Ꭱ ·7	„ „	„ 𐨪. „
6	33·5	Ꭱ ·65	(king helmeted).	„ 𐨀; „ „
7	36·4	Ꭱ ·65	„	„)𐨪(. (king's name written 𐨤𐨗𐨱𐨫, *Lisiasa*.) [Pl. viii. 7.]
			(β) *Bronze; round.* **ΒΑΣΙΛΕΩΣ ΑΝΙΚΗ-ΤΟΥ ΛΥΣ[ΙΟΥ** Bust of bearded Herakles r.; club and palm over shoulder.	𐨤𐨗⁓𐨆𐨱𐨤𐨿𐨗 𐨤𐨩𐨗⁓𐨬 𐨤𐨱𐨫𐨯 (*Māhārajasa apadihātasa Lisikasa*). Elephant r., walking.
8		Æ ·95		below,)𐨪(. [Pl. viii. 8.]

No.	Wt.	Metal. Size.	Obverse.	Reverse.
			(γ) *Bronze; square.*	
			ΒΑΣΙΛΕΩΣ ΑΝΙΚΗ-ΤΟΥ ΛΥΣΙΟΥ Bust of bearded Herakles r.; lion's skin round neck, and club over shoulder.	𐨤𐨪𐨣 𐨤𐨪𐨣 𐨤𐨪𐨣 (*Māhārajasa apadihātasa Lisikasa*). Elephant r., walking.
9		Æ ·75		below, 𐎐 Σ. [Pl. VIII. 9.]
10		Æ ·8		„ „ „
11		Æ ·75		„ „ „
12		Æ ·7		above, 𐎐 .
13		Æ ·75		below, 𐎐 .
14		Æ ·85		„)𝑅(. (king's name written 𐨤𐨪𐨣, *Lisiasa*.)

No.	Wt.	Metal. Size.	Obverse.	Reverse.
			## DIOMEDES.
			(a) Silver ; type, Dioscuri, standing.	
			ΒΑΣΙΛΕΩΣ ΣΩΤΗ- ΡΟΣ ΔΙΟΜΗΔΟΥ Bust of the king r., diad.	𐨤𐨪𐨿𐨗𐨯 (*Maharajasa tradatasa Diya-medasa*). The Dioscuri, facing, holding lances.
1	34·8	Æ ·65		to r., ⌘. [Pl. viii. 10.]
2	35·	Æ ·65	(king helmeted).	to l., „ [Pl. viii. 11.]
			(β) Silver ; type, Dioscuri, mounted.	
			ΒΑΣΙΛΕΩΣ ΣΩΤΗ- ΡΟΣ ΔΙΟΜΗΔΟΥ Bust of the king r., diad.	𐨤𐨪𐨿𐨗𐨯 (*Maharajasa tradatasa Diya-medasa*). The Dioscuri, charging r., holding long lances and palms.
3	33·5	Æ ·65		below, ⌘. [Pl. viii. 12.]
4	33·1	Æ ·65	(king helmeted).	„ „ [Pl. viii 13.]
			(γ) Bronze ; square.	
			ΒΑΣΙΛΕΩΣ ΣΩΤΗ- ΡΟΣ ΔΙΟΜΗΔΟΥ The Dioscuri, facing, holding lances.	𐨤𐨪𐨿𐨗𐨯 (*Māhārajasa tradatasa Diya-medasa*). Indian bull r.
5		Æ ·8		below, ⌘. [Pl. viii. 14.]
6		Æ ·85		„ Σ ⊠.
7		Æ ·85		„ Σ.
8		Æ ·75		„ „

No.	Wt.	Metal. Size.	Obverse.	Reverse.
				ARCHEBIUS.
				(a) *Silver.*
			ΒΑΣΙΛΕΩΣ ΔΙΚΑΙ-ΟΥ ΝΙΚΗΦΟΡΟΥ ΑΡΧΕΒΙΟΥ Bust of the king r., diad.	𐨀𐨤𐨿𐨪 (*Māhārajasa dhramikasa jayadharasa Arkhebiyasa*). Zeus, facing, clad in himation; holds long sceptre in l. hand, and hurls thunderbolt with r.
1	139·	Æ 1·05		to l., ⋈. [I. O. C. Pl. ix. 1.]
2	36·	Æ ·7		to r., 曰. [Pl. ix. 2.]
3	36·3	Æ ·65	(king helmeted).	„ „ [Pl. ix. 3.]
			ΒΑΣΙΛΕΩΣ ΔΙΚΑΙ-ΟΥ ΝΙΚΗΦΟΡΟΥ ΑΡΧΕΒΙΟΥ Bust of the king l., diad., wearing aegis and thrusting with spear.	𐨀𐨤𐨿𐨪 (*Māhārajasa dhramikasa jayadharasa Arkhebiyasa*). Zeus, facing, clad in himation; holds long sceptre in l. hand, and hurls thunderbolt with r.
4	147·6	Æ 1·	(king helmeted).	to l., ⊕. [I. O. C. Pl. ix. 4.]
5	34·4	Æ ·7		to l., ℞ ; to r., ⋈. [I. O. C. Pl. ix. 5.]
				(β) *Bronze; round.*
			ΒΑΣΙΛΕΩΣ ΔΙΚΑΙ-ΟΥ ΝΙΚΗΦΟΡΟΥ ΑΡΧΕΒΙΟΥ Nike l., holding wreath and palm.	𐨀𐨤𐨿𐨪 (*Māhārajasa dhramikasa jayadharasa Arkhebiyasa*). Owl r.
6		Æ 1·		to r., ⋈. [Pl. ix. 6.]

No.	Wt.	Metal. Size.	Obverse.	Reverse.
				(γ) *Bronze ; square.*
			ΒΑΣΙΛΕΩΣ ΔΙΚΑΙ-•Υ ΝΙΚΗΦ•Ρ•Υ ΑΡΧΕΒΙ•Υ Elephant r.	ᎢᎶᏃᎳᎽ ᎢᏂᎠᏃ ᎢᎽᎶᛈ ᎢᎠᏫᏆᎮ𐤟 (*Māhārajasa dhramikasa jayadharasa Arkhebiyasa*). Owl r.
7		Æ 1·		below, 𐎧. [Pl. ix. 7.]
8		Æ ·9		„ 𐎧. [I. O. C.]

F

No.	Wt.	Metal. Size.	Obverse.	Reverse.
			APOLLODOTUS I.	
			(a) Silver; round; Attic weight.	
			ΒΑΣΙΛΕΩΣ ΑΠΟΛ-ΛΟΔΟΤΟΥ ΣΩΤΗΡΟΣ Elephant r., band round body.	ᛏᛉᛌᛩ ᛏᛟᛌᛍᛏᛡᛒ ᛏᛦᛋᛁᛞᛩ (*Māhārajasa Apaladatasa tradatasa*). Indian bull r.
1	31·1	Æ ·6		[Pl. ix. 8.]
2	30·8	Æ ·6		[I. O. C.]
			(β) Silver; square; Indian weight.	
			ΒΑΣΙΛΕΩΣ ΑΠΟΛ-ΛΟΔΟΤΟΥ ΣΩΤΗΡΟΣ Elephant r., band round body.	ᛏᛉᛌᛩ ᛏᛟᛌᛍᛏᛡᛒ ᛏᛦᛋᛁᛞᛩ (*Māhārajasa Apaladatasa tradatasa*). Indian bull r.
3	37·9	Æ ·65	below, ℞.	below, Δ. (ᛏᛉᛌᛩ in inscr.) [Pl. ix. 9.]
4	37·8	Æ ·65	„ „	„ C. „
5	37·8	Æ ·65	„ „	„ ω. „
6	37·7	Æ ·6	„ Ⱥ.	„ Ꞧ.
7	38·	Æ ·6	„ „	„ „ [I. O. C.]
8	36·3	Æ ·65	„ „	„ A.
9	37·5	Æ ·65	„ ᚻ.	„ ᚻ.
10	38·	Æ ·65	„ Ⱳ.	(ꝋ on bull's hump.)
11	37·9	Æ ·6	„ „	„ [I. O. C.]
12	18·3	Æ ·5	below, ΞΕ.	[I. O. C.]

No.	Wt.	Metal. Size.	Obverse.	Reverse.
			(γ) *Bronze; square.*	
			ΒΑΣΙΛΕΩΣ ΑΠΟΛ-ΛΟΔΟΤΟΥ ΣΩΤΗ-ΡΟΣ Apollo, laur., facing; holds in r. hand, arrow; in l., bow.	(*Māhārajasa Apaladatasa trada-tasa*). Tripod on stand, in square of dots.
13		Æ ·9		[Pl. ɪx. 10.]
14		Æ ·95		[I. O. C.]
15		Æ ·85		to r., Κ.
16		Æ ·85	to l., ᛦ.	„ ᛦ.
17		Æ ·95		„ ⋀ᛤ.
18		Æ ·9		„ „ [I. O. C.]
19		Æ ·9		„ „
20		Æ ·9		„ ᛘ.
21		Æ ·9		„ ⵣ. [I. O. C.]
22		Æ 1·		„ ⵣ. „
23		Æ ·9		„ ᛤ. „
24		Æ ·75		„ „ [Pl. ɪx. 11.]

No.	Wt.	Metal. Size.	Obverse.	Reverse.
			ΒΑΣΙΛΕΩΣ ΑΠΟΛ-ΛΟΔΟΤΟΥ ΣΩΤΗ-ΡΟΣ Apollo, laur., facing; holds in r. hand arrow; in l., bow.	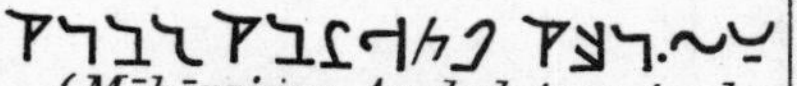 � inscription (*Māhārajasa Apaladatasa tradatasa*). Tripod on stand, in square of dots.
25		Æ ·9		[I. O. C.]
26		Æ ·85	to l., **EI**.	to l., ◻ .
27		Æ ·95	„ „	„ „
28		Æ ·9	„ Ⅰ̄A .	„ ⋈ .
29		Æ ·9		to r., Ƶ .
30		Æ ·9		„ A̅ΕΡ (?)
31		Æ ·8		to l., ℔ . [I. O. C. Pl. ix. 12.]
32		Æ ·7		to r., Ṃ .
33		Æ ·7	(inscr. blundered.)	„ „ [I. O. C.]
34		Æ ·75		„ Ṃ .
35		Æ ·9	(„)	„ „ [I. O. C.]
36		Æ ·75		to l., „
37		Æ ·65	(„)	to r., **M** .
38		Æ ·7		„ ⊞ .
			(δ) *Bronze; square; perhaps of Apollodotus.*	
			Indian bull r., in square of dots.	Tripod, in square of dots.
39		Æ ·5		[I. O. C. Pl. ix. 13.]

No.	Wt.	Metal. Size.	Obverse.	Reverse.
			## APOLLODOTUS II., PHILOPATOR. (a) *Silver.* ΒΑΣΙΛΕΩΣ ΜΕΓΑ-ΛΟΥ ΣΩΤΗΡΟΣ ΚΑΙ ΦΙΛΟΠΑΤΟ-ΡΟΣ ΑΠΟΛΛΟΔΟ-ΤΟΥ Bust of the king r., diad.	ⵣⵣⵣⵣ (*Maharajasa tradatasa Apalada-tasa*). Pallas l., holding in l. hand aegis, and with r. hurling thunderbolt.
1	128·5	Æ1·15		to l., ✠. [Pl. x. 1.]
			ΒΑΣΙΛΕΩΣ ΣΩΤΗ-ΡΟΣ ΚΑΙ ΦΙΛΟ-ΠΑΤΟΡΟΣ ΑΠΟΛ-ΛΟΔΟΤΟΥ Similar bust.	Similar.
2	37·2	Æ ·75		to l., ✠. [Pl. x. 2.]
3	37·3	Æ ·65		to l., uncertain letter; to r., ⋈. [Pl. x. 3.]
4	36·1	Æ ·7		to r., ⋈.
5	36·	Æ ·7		„ Λ̣.
6	36·8	Æ ·7		„ Ⱥ.
			ΒΑΣΙΛΕΩΣ ΣΩΤΗ-ΡΟΣ ΑΠΟΛΛΟΔΟ-ΤΟΥ Similar bust.	Similar.
7	35·4	Æ ·65		to l., ⅄; to r., ⚶.
8	37·8	Æ ·6		[I. "O. C." Pl. x. 4.]

No.	Wt.	Metal. Size.	Obverse.	Reverse.
			(β) Bronze ; round.	
			ΒΑΣΙΛΕΩΣ ΣΩΤΗ-ΡΟΣ ΑΠΟΛΛΟΔΟ-ΤΟΥ Apollo r., clad in chlamys and boots, holding with both hands an arrow ; a quiver at his shoulder.	ⵐⵐⵐⵐ ⵐⵐⵐ ⵐⵐⵐ *(Maharajasa tradatasa Apalada-tasa).* Tripod.
9	Æ 1·25		to l., ⚛.	to l., ⵐ; to r., ⵐ.
10	Æ 1·05		„ „	„ „ „ „ [Pl. x. 5.]
			(γ) Bronze ; square.	
			ΒΑΣΙΛΕΩΣ ΣΩΤΗ-ΡΟΣ ΑΠΟΛΛΟΔΟ-ΤΟΥ Apollo facing, clad in chlamys and boots ; quiver behind shoulder ; holds in l. hand, bow ; in r., arrow, which rests on the ground.	ⵐⵐⵐⵐ ⵐⵐⵐ ⵐⵐⵐ *(Maharajasa tradatasa Apalada-tasa).* Tripod.
11·	Æ 1·			to l., ⊞; to r., ⵐ. [Pl. x. 6.]
			Same inscr. Apollo r., clad in chlamys and boots ; holds with both hands an arrow ; a quiver at his shoulder.	Same inscr. Tripod.
12	Æ 1·1			to l., ⵐ ; to r., club. *(flan* of coin round). [Pl. x. 7.]
13	Æ ·95			mons. obscure.
14	Æ ·8			to l., ⵐ ; to r., ⚛. (type within square of dots.)
15	Æ ·8			to r., ⵐ. [I. O. C. Pl. x. 8.]

No.	Wt.	Metal. Size.	Obverse.	Reverse.
			ΒΑΣΙΛΕΩΣ ΣΩΤΗ-ΡΟΣ ΚΑΙ ΦΙΛΟ-ΠΑΤΟΡΟΣ ΑΠΟΛ-ΛΟΔΟΤΟΥ Apollo r., clad in chlamys and boots; holds in r. hand, arrow; in l., bow.	𐨎𐨎𐨎 𐨎𐨎𐨎 𐨎𐨎𐨎 (*Maharajasa tradatasa Apalada-tasa*). Tripod.
16		Æ ·8	(type within square of fillet-pattern.)	to r., mon. (type within square of fillet-pattern).
17		Æ ·8	,,	,, 𐎀. ,,
			ΒΑΣΙΛΕΩΣ ΣΩΤΗ-ΡΟΣ ΚΑΙ ΦΙΛΟ-ΠΑΤΟΡΟΣ ΑΠΟΛ-ΛΟΔΟΤΟΥ Similar type.	𐨎𐨎𐨎 𐨎𐨎𐨎 𐨎𐨎𐨎 (*Maharajasa tradatasa Apalada-tasa*). Tripod.
18		Æ ·65		to r., 𐎀. [Pl. x. 9.]
19		Æ ·6		,, ,,
			Similar type, within square of fillet-pattern.	𐨎𐨎𐨎 𐨎𐨎𐨎 𐨎𐨎𐨎 (*Maharajasa tradatasa Apalada-tasa*). Diadema.
20		Æ ·6		

No.	Wt.	Metal. Size.	Obverse.	Reverse.
				STRATO I.
				(a) Silver.
			ΒΑΣΙΛΕΩΣ ΕΠΙΦΑ-ΝΟΥΣ ΣΩΤΗΡΟΣ ΣΤΡΑΤΩΝΟΣ Bust of the king r., diad.	𐨤𐨪𐨗 𐨀𐨬𐨼𐨜 𐨤𐨪𐨟 (*Māhārajasa pratichhasa tradatasa Stratasa*). Pallas l., holding with l. hand aegis, and with r. hurling thunderbolt.
1	133·3	Æ1·05	(king wears helmet.)	to l., 中. [Pl. x. 10.]
2	31·3	Æ ·7		to l., 中.
3	36·2	Æ ·7		„ ℞. [Pl. x. 11.]
4	33·3	Æ ·65		„ „
			ΒΑΣΙΛΕΩΣ ΣΩΤΗ-ΡΟΣ ΣΤΡΑΤΩΝΟΣ Bust of the king r., diad.	𐨤𐨪𐨗 𐨀𐨬𐨼𐨜 (*Māhārajasa tradatasa Stratasa*). Similar type.
5	35·8	Æ ·7	(king helmeted.)	to l., 𐊦. [Pl. x. 12.]
6	35·5	Æ ·6		„ 𐌆; to r., 𐊦. (semi-barbarous.)
7	37·6	Æ ·65		„ 𐊦; „ 𐊦. [I. O. C. Pl. x. 13.]
8	35·4	Æ ·6		„ 𐊦; „ „ 𐊦. „
9	† 34·4	Æ ·6	inscr. . . . . ΡΟΝΟΣΑ . . . ΝΟΣ	„ „ „ „ 𐊦. „ [Pl. x. 14.]
10	32·2	Æ ·65		„ 𐊦; „ „ 𐊦. „ [I. O. C.] (last line of inscr. *padayashasa*?).

* Or 𐨗 *cha*, *prachichhasa*.

† This is one of the coins sometimes wrongly given to an imaginary king, Rosastonos.

No.	Wt.	Metal. Size.	Obverse.	Reverse.
			ΒΑΣΙΛΕΩΣ ΣΩΤΗ-ΡΟΣ ΔΙΚΑΙΟΥ ΣΤΡΑΤΩΝΟΣ Bust of the king r., diad.	𐨀𐨤𐨢𐨿 𐨤𐨭𐨿𐨢 𐨤𐨩𐨂.~𐨩 𐨤𐨢𐨸 (*Māhārajasa tradaṭasa dhramikasa Stratasa*). Pallas r., holding in l. hand aegis, and with r. hurling thunderbolt.
11	32·7	Æ ·65		to l., ⟨symbol⟩. [Pl. xi. 1.]
			(β) *Bronze; round.*	
			ΒΑΣΙΛΕΩΣ ΕΠΙΦΑ-ΝΟΥΣ ΣΩΤΗΡΟΣ ΣΤΡΑΤΩΝΟΣ Bust of Apollo r., laur.; hair in queue.	𐨤𐨭𐨿𐨢 𐨤𐨩𐨿𐨯 𐨤𐨩𐨂.~𐨩 𐨤𐨢𐨸 (*Māhārajasa pratichhasa tradaṭasa Stratasa*). Bow and quiver, with strap.
12		Æ 1·		to l., ⟨symbol⟩. [Pl. xi. 2.]
			(γ) *Bronze; square; type, Apollo.*	
			ΒΑΣΙΛΕΩΣ ΕΠΙΦΑ-ΝΟΥΣ ΣΩΤΗΡΟΣ ΣΤΡΑΤΩΝΟΣ Apollo, facing; holds in r. hand, arrow; in l., bow.	𐨤𐨭𐨿𐨢 𐨤𐨩𐨿𐨯 𐨤𐨩𐨂.~𐨩 𐨤𐨢𐨸 (*Māhārajasa pratichhasa tradaṭasa Stratasa*). Tripod-lebes, on stand.
13		Æ ·95		to l., ⟨symbol⟩; to r., ⟨symbol⟩. [I. O. C. Pl. xi. 3.]
14		Æ ·9		„ ⟨symbol⟩. [I. O. C.]
15		Æ ·9		„ ⟨symbol⟩.
16		Æ ·85		„ ⟨symbol⟩; to r., ⟨symbol⟩ and mon. [I. O. C.]

G

No.	Wt.	Metal. Size.	Obverse.	Reverse.
				(δ) *Bronze ; square ; type, Nike.*
			ΒΑΣΙΛΕΩΣ ΣΩΤΗ-ΡΟΣ ΣΤΡΑΤΩΝΟΣ Bust of bearded Hera-kles r.; over shoulder, club bound with taenia.	ᛣᛚᛉ ᛣᛚᛚᛉ ᛣᛃᛚ.~ᛃ (*Māhārajasa tradatasa Stratasa*). Nike r., holds wreath and palm.
17		Æ ·8		to r., 𐰗. [I. O. C. Pl. xi. 4.]
18		Æ ·85		„ Σ. [I. O. C.]
19		Æ ·8		„ „
			ΒΑΣΙΛΕΩΣ ΣΩΤΗ-ΡΟΣ ΔΙΚΑΙΟΥ ΣΤΡΑΤΩΝΟΣ Similar type.	ᛣᚼᛃᛉ ᛣᛚᛚᛉ ᛣᛃᛚ~ᛑ ᛣᛚᛉ (*Maharajasa tradatasa dhramikasa Stratasa*). Similar type.
20		Æ ·9		to r., 𐰗. [Pl. xi. 5.]

No.	Wt.	Metal. Size.	Obverse.	Reverse.

AGATHOCLEIA, WITH STRATO.

(a) *Bronze; square.*

			ΒΑΣΙΛΙΣΣΗΣ ΘΕΟ-ΤΡΟΠΟΥ ΑΓΑΘΟ-ΚΛΕΙΑΣ Bust of the Queen r., helmeted.	𐨤𐨯𐨪 𐨤𐨪𐨟 𐨤𐨩𐨟𐨿 𐨤𐨟 (*Maharajasa tradatasa dhramikasa Stratasa*). Herakles seated l. on rock; holds in r. hand, club, which rests on knee (type of Euthydemus).
1		Æ ·8		to l., ⚒. [Pl. XI. 6.]
2		Æ ·8		„ „ [I. O. C.]

No.	Wt.	Metal. Size.	Obverse.	Reverse.
				MENANDER.
				(a) *Silver.*
			ΒΑΣΙΛΕΩΣ ΣΩΤΗ-ΡΟΣ ΜΕΝΑΝΔΡΟΥ Bust of the king r., diad.	(*Māhārajasa trādatasa Mena-drāsa*). Pallas l., holding in l. hand aegis, and with r. hurling thunderbolt.
1	150·9	Æ 1·05		to l., Σ; to r.,)?(. [I. O. C.]
2	148 6	Æ 1·		„ „ „ „
3	149·	Æ 1·		„ [Pl. xi. 7.]
4	142·7	Æ 1·	(king helmeted).	„ „ „ Σ· [I. O. C.]
5	149·8	Æ 1·1	„	„ „ „ „ [Pl. xi. 8.]
6	38·1	Æ ·6	(king helmeted).	to r., Ɛ·
7	37·	Æ ·7	„	„)?(·
8	37·5	Æ ·7	„	„ ℞·
9	34·8	Æ ·6	„	to l., „
10	37·8	Æ ·65	„	to r., ⊛·
11	38·	Æ ·65	„	„ „ [Pl. xi. 9.]

No.	Wt.	Metal. Size.	Obverse.	Reverse.
			ΒΑΣΙΛΕΩΣ ΣΩΤΗ-ΡΟΣ ΜΕΝΑΝΔΡΟΥ Bust of the king r., diad.	ᛕᛐᛁᛌᛁ ᛐᛦᛎᛁ.〜ᴗ (*Māhārajasa* ᛎ.ᛌᛌᚒ *trādatasa Mena-drāsa*). Pallas l., holding in l. hand aegis, and with r. hurling thunderbolt.
12	37·8	Æ ·7	(king helmeted).	to r., ⊕.
13	37·8	Æ ·7	,,	,, ,,
14	39·	Æ ·7		[I. O. C.]
15	34·8	Æ ·65		to l., ⚛.
16	33·6	Æ ·7		to r., ,,
17	37·6	Æ ·7		,, ⋈.
18	37·4	Æ ·7		,, ⋈.
19	38·	Æ ·65		,, E.
20	34·1	Æ ·75		to l., ⊟.
21	37·5	Æ ·65		,, ,, ; to r., ⋈.
22	36·	Æ ·65		,, ⋈.
23	37·7	Æ ·65		,, ,, [I. O. C.]
24	37·3	Æ ·65		,,)የ(.
25	37·	Æ ·7		to r., ,, [Pl. XI. 10.]

No.	Wt.	Metal. Size.	Obverse.	Reverse.
			ΒΑΣΙΛΕΩΣ ΣΩΤΗ-ΡΟΣ ΜΕΝΑΝΔΡΟΥ Bust of the king r., diad.	ᛔᛋᚾᛚᚴᛈᛋᛁᛌ (*Māhārajasa* ᛈᛚᚴᚥ *trādatasa Mena-drāsa*). Pallas l., holding in l. hand aegis, and with r. hurling thunderbolt.
26	36·3	Æ ·65		to l.,)?(; to r., Γ. [I. O. C.]
27	39·	Æ ·7		„ „ „ E·
28	38·3	Æ ·7		„ Σ; „)?(·
29	38·	Æ ·75		to r., ⌨·
30	38·7	Æ ·7		„ „
			Same inscr. Bust of the king l., wearing aegis and thrusting with spear.	Similar.
31	36·6	Æ ·7		to l., ☒·
32	37·1	Æ ·65		to r., ᛗ·
33	37·3	Æ ·65		„ ᛗ·
34	37·8	Æ ·7		„ ⌨·
35	38·	Æ ·75		„ ᛗ·

No.	Wt.	Metal. Size.	Obverse.	Reverse.
			ΒΑΣΙΛΕΩΣ ΣΩΤΗ-ΡΟΣ ΜΕΝΑΝΔΡΟΥ Bust of the king l., wearing aegis and thrusting with spear.	ᏋᏋᏋ (*Māhārajasa trādatasa Menadrāsa*). Pallas r., holding in l. hand aegis, and with r. hurling thunderbolt.
36	38·2	Æ ·7		to l., ⊕.
37	38·	Æ ·7		,, ,,
38	37·8	Æ ·65		,, ᛗ.
39	37·7	Æ ·7		to r., ⊕. [I. O. C. Pl. xi. 11.]
40	38·2	Æ ·65		,, ,,
41	37·8	Æ ·65		to l., ᛗ.
42	37·9	Æ ·7		,, ᛗ.
43	38·2	Æ ·65		,, ᛝ.

(β) *Bronze; square; with portrait.*

No.	Wt.	Metal. Size.	Obverse.	Reverse.
			ΒΑΣΙΛΕΩΣ ΣΩΤΗ-ΡΟΣ ΜΕΝΑΝΔΡΟΥ Bust of the king l., diad., wearing aegis and thrusting with spear.	ᏋᏋᏋ (*Māhārajasa tradatasa Menadrāsa*). Pallas r., holding in l. hand aegis, and with r. hurling thunderbolt.
44		Æ ·85		to r., ⊕.
45		Æ ·8		,, ,,
46		Æ ·9		,, ᛟ. [I. O. C. Pl. xi. 12.]

No.	Wt.	Metal. Size.	Obverse.	Reverse.
			(γ) *Bronze ; square ; with head of Pallas.*	
			ΒΑΣΙΛΕΩΣ ΣΩΤΗ- ΡΟΣ ΜΕΝΑΝΔΡΟΥ Bust of Pallas r., wearing crested helmet.	ꓼꓶꓼꓶ ꓶꓬꓱꓶ.ᴖꓱ (*Māhārajasa* ꓟ ꓶꓚꙍ *tradatasa Mena-drasa*). Horse r., prancing.
47		Æ 1·1		below, ⊕.
			Similar.	Same inscr. Nike r. ; holds wreath and palm.
48		Æ ·9		to r., ᚱᚳ . [I. O. C.]
49		Æ ·8		„ ⊕. [I. O. C. Pl. xi. 13.]
50		Æ ·75		„ Ɛ̶.
51		Æ ·85		„ ⊕.
52		Æ ·7		„ „
53		Æ ·8		„ ₥.
54		Æ ·7		„ „
55		Æ ·8		„ ⋈.
			Similar.	Same inscr. Nike l. ; holds wreath and palm.
56		Æ ·75		to l., ⊕; to r., **B** . [I. O. C.]
57		Æ ·8		„ ⊕; „ „ [Pl. xii. 1.]
58		Æ ·75		„. **B** . [I. O. C.]

No.	Wt.	Metal. Size.	Obverse.	Reverse.
			ΒΑΣΙΛΕΩΣ ΣΩΤΗ-ΡΟΣ ΜΕΝΑΝΔΡΟΥ Bust of Pallas r., wearing crested helmet.	ꓕ.ᒐ ꕛꞱ ꓔᒣᒐᒐ ꓔ꓆ᒹ.~ꓬ (*Māhārajasa tradatasa Menadrāsa*). Round buckler; Gorgonhead in the midst.
59		Æ ·85		below, **M**. [Pl. XII. 2.]
60		Æ ·85		„ **M**.
61		Æ ·85		to l., **M**.
62		Æ ·9		„ „ [I. O. C. Pl. XII. 3.]
			Similar.	Same inscr. Owl r.
63		Æ ·8		to r., **M**. [I. O. C. Pl. XII. 4.]

(δ) *Bronze ; square ; Apolline types.*

No.	Wt.	Metal. Size.	Obverse.	Reverse.
			ΒΑΣΙΛΕΩΣ ΣΩΤΗ-ΡΟΣ ΜΕΝΑΝΔΡΟΥ Ox-head, facing.	ꓕ.ᒐ ꕛꞱ ꓔᒣᒐ.ᒐ ꓔ꓆ᒹ.~ꓬ (*Māhārajasa trādatasa Menadrāsa*). Tripod-lebes.
64		Æ ·9		to l., **R**.
65		Æ ·9		„ „
66		Æ ·9		„ ꓴ ; to r., **M**. [Pl. XII. 5.]

H

No.	Wt.	Metal. Size.	Obverse.	Reverse.
			(ε) *Bronze ; square ; Herakleian types.*	
			ΒΑΣΙΛΕΩΣ ΣΩΤΗ-ΡΟΣ ΜΕΝΑΝΔΡΟΥ Elephant's head r., bell round neck.	Ͳ·ↄↄϢ Ͳ〜Ͻ·ↄ Ͳϟϡ·〜Ⴤ (*Māhārajasa trādatasa Mena-drāsa*). Club upwards.
67		Æ ·65		to l., ⊠; to r., **A**.
68		Æ ·55		„ „ „ „ [Pl. XII. 6.]
69		Æ ·6		„ **A**; „ ⊕.
70		Æ ·6		„ „ „ „ [I. O. C.]
71		Æ ·55	below, **A**.	to r., Ͳ.
72		Æ ·55	„ **O**.	„ ⊕.
			(ζ) *Bronze ; square ; type, wheel.*	
			ΒΑΣΙΛΕΩΣ ΣΩΤΗ-ΡΟΣ ΜΕΝΑΝΔΡΟΥ Wheel.	Ͳ·ↄↄϢ Ͳ〜Ͻ·ↄ Ͳϟϡ·〜Ⴤ (*Māhārajasa trādatasa Mena-drāsa*). Palm.
73		Æ ·5		to r., mon. [I. O. C. Pl. XII. 7.]
			(η) *Bronze ; square ; with title* δίκαιός.	
			ΒΑΣΙΛΕΩΣ ΔΙΚΑΙ-•Υ ΜΕΝΑΝΔΡ•Υ Pallas l., holds patera ? and spear, against which leans shield.	Ͳ·ↄↄϢ ͲᚺΨϟ Ͳϟϡ·〜Ⴤ (*Māhārajasa dhramikasa Mena-drāsa*) Maneless Indian lion l.
74		Æ ·85		below, 中.

No.	Wt.	Metal. Size.	Obverse.	Reverse.

EPANDER.

(α) *Bronze.*

ΒΑΣΙΛΕΩΣ ΝΙΚΗ-ΦΟΡΟΥ ΕΠΑΝΔΡΟΥ
Nike advancing r.; holds wreath and palm.

𐨤·𐨫𐨱𐨩 𐨤𐨪𐨩𐨫𐨱 𐨤𐨩𐨪𐨰𐨮 (*Māharajasa jayadharasa Epadrāsa*). Indian bull r.

below, Ɛ Ʀ . [I. O. C. Pl. xii 8.]

| 1 | | Æ ·9 | | |

DIONYSIUS.

(α) *Silver.*

ΒΑΣΙΛΕΩΣ ΣΩΤΗ-ΡΟΣ ΔΙΟΝΥΣΙΟΥ
Bust of the king r., diad.

𐨤𐨪𐨱𐨰𐨮 𐨤𐨩𐨪𐨰𐨪 (*Maharajasa* 𐨤𐨫𐨿𐨝𐨫𐨱𐨮 *tradatasa Dianisiyasa*). Pallas l.; holding in l. hand, aegis; and with r., hurling thunderbolt.

to r., 🜍. [I. O. C. Pl. xii. 9.]

| 1 | 38· | Æ ·7 | | |

(β) *Bronze.*

ΒΑΣΙΛΕΩΣ ΣΩΤΗ-ΡΟΣ ΔΙΟΝΥΣΙΟΥ
Apollo r., clad in chlamys and boots; holds in both hands an arrow; a quiver at his back.

𐨤𐨫𐨿𐨝𐨫𐨱𐨮 𐨤𐨪𐨱𐨰𐨮 *Dianisiyasa*). Tripod.

to l., 𐨱; to r., 𐨨. [I. O. C.]

| 2 | | Æ ·85 | | |
| 3 | | Æ ·8 | | mons. obscure. |

No.	Wt.	Metal. Size.	Obverse.	Reverse.
				ZOILUS.
				(α) *Silver; with title* δικαιός.
			ΒΑΣΙΛΕΩΣ ΔΙΚΑΙ-ΟΥ ΙΩΙΛΟΥ Bust of the king r., diad.	𐨤𐨧𐨿𐨪 𐨧𐨱𐨬𐨏 𐨤𐨗 ~ᵕ (*Māhārajasa dhramikasa Jhoïlasa*). Herakles facing, crowned with ivy; holds in r. hand, wreath; in l., club and lion's skin.
1	37·4	Æ ·7		to l., Ⱨ. [Pl. xii. 10.]
2	38·5	Æ ·65		„ 𐊈. [I. O. C.]
				(β) *Silver; with title* σωτήρ.
			ΒΑΣΙΛΕΩΣ ΣΩΤΗ-ΡΟΣ ΙΩΙΛΟΥ Bust of the king r., diad.	𐨤𐨣𐨿𐨩 𐨤𐨩𐨏~ᵕ (*Maharajasa* 𐨤𐨧𐨿𐨪 *tradatasa* *Jhoïlasa*). Pallas l.; holding in l. hand, aegis; and with r., hurling thunderbolt.
3	34·8	Æ ·65		to l., 𐌶; to r., 🜨. [I. O. C. Pl. xii. 11.]
4	37·4	Æ ·65	Z in inscr.	„ 𐌷; „ „ [I. O. C.]
5	37·6	Æ ·8	„	„ ⵏ; „ „ „
6	36·6	Æ ·6	„	„ ꟼ; „ 目 𐋠.
7	34·4	Æ ·7	„	„ „ .~.
8	38·2	Æ ·7	„	„ 𐌈. [I. O. C.]

No.	Wt.	Metal. Size.	Obverse.	Reverse.
			(γ) *Bronze; round.*	
			ΒΑΣΙΛΕΩΣ ΣΩΤΗ-ΡΟΣ ΙΩΙΛΟΥ Apollo r., clad in chlamys and boots; holds in both hands an arrow; a quiver at his back; in field l., small elephant.	𐨤𐨷𐨫 𐨤𐨩𐨫𐨯 (*Maharajasa* 𐨤𐨿𐨿 *tradatasa Jhoïlasa*). Tripod.
9		Æ 1·25		to l., 𐨿; to r., 𐨪. [Pl. xii. 12.]
			Elephant r.	Similar.
10		Æ ·75		to l., 𐨆; to r., 𐨪. (double-struck).
			(δ) *Bronze; square.*	
			ΒΑΣΙΛΕΩΣ ΣΩΤΗ-ΡΟΣ ΙΠΙΛΟΥ Apollo r., clad in chlamys and boots; holds in both hands an arrow; a quiver at his back.	𐨤𐨿 𐨤𐨷𐨫 𐨤𐨩𐨫𐨯 (*Maharajasa tradatasa Jhoïlasa*). Tripod.
11		Æ 1·	to l., 𐨿 .	to l., 𐨩; to r., 𐨱. [Pl. xii. 13.]

No.	Wt.	Metal. Size.	Obverse.	Reverse.
			APOLLOPHANES.	
			(a) *Silver.*	
			BAΣIΛEΩΣ ΣΩTH-POΣ AΠOΛΛOΦA-NOY (*sic*) Bust of the king r., helmeted; diadem tied round the helmet.	ꓓꓶꓶꓵ ꓑꓬꓶꓩ∿ꓴ (*Maharajasa tradatasa Apulaphanasa*). Pallas l.; holding in l. hand, aegis; and with r. hurling thunderbolt.
1	36·3	Æ ·65		to l., ✗; to r., ᗺ. [Pl. XIII. 1.]
2	37·8	Æ ·65		„ „ „ „ [I. O. C.]
			ARTEMIDORUS.	
			(a) *Bronze; square.*	
			BAΣIΛEΩΣ ANI-KH[TOYAP]TEMI-ΔΩPOY Artemis, facing; holds in l., bow, and with r., draws arrow from quiver at her back.	ꓑꓬ∿ꓥ⏌ꓶ ꓑꓬꓩ.∿ꓪ ꓑꓶꓵꓦ�ꓶ (*Māhārajasa apadihatasa Artemidorasa*). Humped bull r.
1		Æ ·8		below, ꓧ. [Pl. XIII. 2.]

No.	Wt.	Metal. Size.	Obverse.	Reverse.
			ANTIMACHUS II., NICEPHORUS.	
			(a) *Silver.*	
			ΒΑΣΙΛΕΩΣ ΝΙΚΗ-ΦΟΡΟΥ ΑΝΤΙΜΑ-ΧΟΥ Nike l. ; holds palm and wreath.	ᖷᖲ (*Māhārajasa jayadharasa Amti-mākhasa*). The king, wearing causia, diadem, and chlamys, on horseback r.
1	37·6	Æ ·65	to l., ⊕.	[Pl. XIII. 3.]
2	37·5	Æ ·65	„ „	
3	37·8	Æ ·65	„ ⧈.	
4	38·4	Æ ·7	„ „	[I. O. C.]
5	37·8	Æ ·7	„ ⋈.	
6	37·5	Æ ·6	„ „	
7	37·8	Æ ·65	„ „	[I. O. C.]
8	38·3	Æ ·65	„ ⋈.	
9	36·7	Æ ·7	„ „	
			(β) *Bronze; square.*	
			ΒΑΣΙΛΕΩΣ ΝΙΚΗ-ΦΟΡΟΥ ΑΝΤΙΜΑ-ΧΟΥ Aegis : in the midst, Gorgon-head.	(*Māhārajasa jayadharasa Amti-mākhasa*). Wreath and palm.
10		Æ ·8		below, ⧈. [Pl. XIII. 4.]

No.	Wt.	Metal. Size.	Obverse.	Reverse.
				PHILOXENUS.
				(*a*) *Silver ; round.*
			ΒΑΣΙΛΕΩΣ ΑΝΙΚΗ-ΤΟΥ ΦΙΛΟΞΕΝΟΥ Bust of the king r., diad.	𐨤𐨗~𐨱/𐨗 𐨤𐨗𐨗.~𐨤 𐨤𐨟𐨤𐨹𐨣 (*Māhārajasa apadihatasa Philasinasa*). King, helmeted and diad., on horseback r. ; horse prancing.
1	151·4	Æ1·05		below, Φ . (𐨹 for 𐨱 in inscr.).
2	150·8	Æ1·2		„ ⊞ . [Pl. xiii. 5.]
3	149·	Æ1·05	(king helmeted).	„ Σ ⊠ . [Pl. xiii. 6.]
				(*β*) *Silver ; square.*
			ΒΑΣΙΛΕΩΣ ΑΝΙΚΗ-ΤΟΥ ΦΙΛΟΞΕΝΟΥ Bust of the king r., diad.	𐨤𐨗~𐨱/𐨗 𐨤𐨗𐨗.~𐨤 𐨤𐨟𐨤𐨹𐨣 (*Māhārajasa apadihatasa Phila*sinasa*). King, helmeted and diad., on horseback r. ; horse prancing.
4	36·8	Æ ·65		below, ⋈ . [I. O. C. Pl. xiii. 7.]
5	33·3	Æ ·65		„ Σ ⊠ . [I. O. C.]
6	35·	Æ ·7		„ ⊞ .
7	27·3	Æ ·6	(king helmeted).	„ ℞ . [I. O. C. Pl. xiii. 8.]
8	25·	Æ ·7	„	„ ⊡ . (plated).
9	26·	Æ ·6	„	„ ⋈ . „ [I. O. C.]

* Sometimes *lu* for *la.*

No.	Wt.	Metal. Size.	Obverse.	Reverse.
			(γ) *Bronze; square.*	
			ΒΑΣΙΛΕΩΣ ΑΝΙΚΗ-ΤΟΥ ΦΙΛΟΞΕΝΟΥ Sun-god, facing, radiate, clad in chiton, himation, and boots; holds in l. hand long sceptre; r. extended.	𐨀𐨤𐨡 (*Mahārajasa apadihatasa Phila*sinasa*). Nike r.; holds wreath and palm.
10		Æ ·8		to r., ◙. [Pl. xiii. 9.]
			Same inscr. A City l.; in l. hand cornucopiae; r. extended.	Same inscr. Indian bull r.
11		Æ ·85	to l., ▤.	below, Σ.
12		Æ ·8	„ „	„ „
13		Æ ·8	„ ◙.	„ 𐨫. [I. O. C. Pl. xiii. 10.]
14		Æ ·8	„ „	[I. O. C.]
15		Æ ·8	„ „	
16		Æ ·9	„ mon.	„ Φ. „
17		Æ ·8	„ ⊡.	„ Σ. „

* Sometimes *lu* for *la*.

I

No.	Wt.	Metal. Size.	Obverse.	Reverse.

NICIAS.

(a) *Bronze; square.*

BACIΛEШC CШTH-POC NIKIOY Head of the king r., diad.

(or ᛏ∧ᛏ∼∪) ᛏᛃᛏ∼∪] ᛏ⁊ᚻ[ᚠ ᛏ⁊⅄⅄ (*Maharajasa* or *Maharayasa tradatasa Nikiasa*). King, diad. and wearing chlamys, on horseback r.; horse prancing.

[Pl. XIII. 11.]

1   Æ ·8

ΒΑΣΙΛΕΩΣ ΣΩΤΗ-ΡΟΣ ΝΙΚΙΟΥ Similar head.

ᛏ⁊ᚻᚠ ᛏ⁊⅄⅄ ᛏᛃᛏ∼∪ (*Maharajasa tradatasa Nikiasa*). Dolphin twined round anchor.

[Pl. XIII. 12.]

2   Æ ·9

No.	Wt.	Metal. Size.	Obverse.	Reverse.
				HIPPOSTRATUS.
				(α) *Silver; type, City.*
			ΒΑΣΙΛΕΩΣ ΣΩΤΗ-ΡΟΣ ΙΠΠΟΣΤΡΑ-ΤΟΥ Bust of the king r., diad.	𐨤𐨪𐨜𐨿𐨌 𐨤𐨩𐨤𐨯 (*Maharajasa* 𐨤𐨟𐨿𐨢𐨟 *tradatasa Hipastratasa*). City l., wearing modius; holds in l. hand, cornucopiae; r. advanced.
1	146·	Æ1·1		to l., 𐨎; to r., �. [Pl. xiv. 1.]
2	147·7	Æ1·15		„ „ „ „
				(β) *Silver; type, King on horseback.*
			ΒΑΣΙΛΕΩΣ ΜΕΓΑ-ΛΟΥ ΣΩΤΗΡΟΣ ΙΠΠΟΣΤΡΑΤΟΥ Bust of the king r., diad.	𐨤𐨪𐨜 𐨤𐨪𐨜 𐨤𐨩𐨤 𐨤𐨟𐨿𐨢𐨟 𐨤𐨪𐨙 (*Maharajasa tradatasa mahātasa jayamtasa Hipastratasa*). King, diad. and helmeted, wearing chlamys, on horseback r.; horse prancing.
3	139·5	Æ 1·2		below, ⊞.
4	147·	Æ 1·1		to l., 𐨩; to r., Ⓐ; below, 𐨤. [Pl. xiv. 2.]
5	144·	Æ1·05		„ „ „ „ „ 𐨱. [I. Q. C.]
6	34·6	Æ ·75		| to l., 𐨩; to r., Ⓐ; below, 𐨱. [Pl. xiv. 3.]
			Similar.	Similar, horse walking.
7	143·2	Æ1·1		to l., 𐨩; to r., Ⓐ; below, 𐨭. [Pl. xiv. 4.]
8	144·8	Æ1·05		„ „ „ „ „ „
9	143·	Æ1·1		„ „ „ „ „ 𐨤. [I. O. C.]

No.	Wt.	Metal. Size.	Obverse.	Reverse.
			ΒΑΣΙΛΕΩΣ ΣΩΤΗ-ΡΟΣ ΙΠΠΟΣΤΡΑ-ΤΟΥ Bust of the king r., diad.	ᕁᕄ.ᐱᕀ ᕁᕄᕄᕼ ᕁᕀᕄᗐ ᕁᕄ⟋ᕄᕁ (*Maharajasa tradatasa jayaṃtasa Hipastratasa*). King, diad. and helmeted, wearing chlamys, on horseback r.; horse prancing.
10	143·	Æ1·15		below, ✠. [I. O. C. Pl. xiv. 5.]
			(γ) *Bronze; square.*	
			ΒΑΣΙΛΕΩΣ ΣΩΤΗ-ΡΟΣ ΙΠΠΟΣΤΡΑ-ΤΟΥ Triton, facing, his body ending in fish's tails; holds dolphin and rudder.	ᕁᕄ⟋ᕄᕁ ᕁᕄᕄᕼ ᕁᕀᕄᗐ (*Maharajasa tradatasa Hipastra-tasa*). City l., turreted; holds in l. hand, palm; r. advanced.
11		Æ1·05		to l., 𐤈; to r., 𐤟.
12		Æ 1·		„ „ „ „
13		Æ 1·		„ „ „ [I. O. C. Pl. xiv. 6.]
			Same inscr. Apollo r., clad in chlamys; holds arrow in both hands; quiver at shoulder.	Same inscr. Tripod.
14		Æ ·9		to l., 𐤈; to r., 𐤟. [Pl. xiv. 7.]
			Same inscr. Pallas, hel-meted, seated l. on throne; holds in r., taenia; in l., spear.	ᕁᕄ.ᐱᕀ ᕁᕄᕄᕼ ᕁᕀᕄᗐ ᕁᕄ⟋ᕄᕁ (*Maharajasa tradatasa jayaṃtasa Hipastratasa*). Horse l., in square of fillet-pattern.
15		Æ ·85		to l., ✠.
16		Æ ·8		„ „ [I. O. C. Pl. xiv. 8.]
17		Æ ·85		„ „

No.	Wt.	Metal. Size.	Obverse.	Reverse.

AMYNTAS.

(a) Silver; type, Pallas.

| | | | **BAΣIΛEΩΣ NIKA-TOPOΣ AMYNTOY** Bust of the king r., diad., helmeted. | **ፖግΨ? ፖግ⅗Λy ፖyግ.~y** (*Māhārajasa jayadharasa Amitasa*). Pallas l.; holding in l. hand, aegis; and with r. hurling thunderbolt. |
| 1 | 127·2 | Æ 1· | | to l., 🜚.   [Pl. xiv. 9.] |

(β) Silver; type, Zeus.

			BAΣIΛEΩΣ NIKA-TOPOΣ AMYNTOY Bust of the king r., diad.	**ፖግΨ? ፖግ⅗Λy ፖyግ.~y** (*Māhārajasa jayadharasa Amitasa*). Zeus seated l. on throne; in r. hand, Nike; in l., palm and sceptre.
2	33·4	Æ ·65		to l., ⊠.
3	36·2	Æ ·65		to r., „ [I. O. C. Pl. xiv. 10.]

(γ) Bronze; square.

			BAΣIΛEΩΣ NIKA-TOPOΣ AMYNTOY Bearded bust r., radiate, in Phrygian cap; sceptre over shoulder.	**ፖግΨ? ፖግ⅗Λy ፖyግ.~y** (*Māhārajasa jayadharasa Amitasa*). Pallas standing l., her r. hand advanced; in her l., spear and shield.
4		Æ ·8		to l., ⊠.
5		Æ ·8		„ 🜚. [I. O. C. Pl. xiv. 11.]

HERMAEUS.

(a) Silver.

No.	Wt.	Metal. Size.	Obverse.	Reverse.
			ΒΑΣΙΛΕΩΣ ΣΩΤΗ- ΡΟΣ ΕΡΜΑΙΟΥ Bust of the king r., diad.	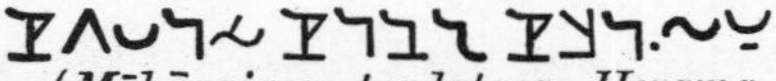 ����‍ (*Mahārajasa tradatasa Heramayasa*). Zeus, laur., seated l. on throne with back; his r. hand advanced; in his l., sceptre.
1	150·7	Æ 1·		to r., ℞. [I. O. C. Pl. xv. 1.]
2	148·6	Æ 1·		„ ⊕.
3	144·1	Æ 1·		„ ℳ.
4	143·3	Æ 1·		„ ⊟. [I. O. C. Pl. xv. 2.]
5	35·4	Æ ·65		to r., ⊞.
6	34·7	Æ ·65		„ „ [I. O. C.]
7	33·8	Æ ·65		„ ⟁.
8	33·	Æ ·65		„ „ „
9	36·	Æ ·65		„ ⊕.
10	36·	Æ ·7		„ ⊠.
11	36·5	Æ ·65		„ ⊠. [Pl. xv. 3.]
12	36·3	Æ ·7		„ ⊠. [I. O. C.]

No.	Wt.	Metal. Size.	Obverse.	Reverse.
			ΒΑΣΙΛΕΩΣ ΣΩΤΗ-ΡΟΣ ΕΡΜΑΙΟΥ Bust of the king r., diad.	𐨤𐨫𐨁𐨯 𐨪𐨗𐨿𐨪 𐨱𐨅𐨪 (*Mahārajasa tradatasa Heramayasa*). Zeus, laur., seated l. on throne with back; his r. hand advanced; in his l., sceptre.
13	32·8	Æ ·65		to r., Ⱥ.
14	34·5	Æ ·6		„ „ [I. O. C.]
15	37·3	Æ ·65		to l., ⬡P.
16	35·	Æ ·65		„ M; to r., ◹. [I. O. C.]
17	36·3	Æ ·6		„ „ „ „
18	37·5	Æ ·6		„ ✠.
19	50·	Æ ·7 (plated)		„ „
			ΒΑΣΙΛΕΩΣ ΣΩΤΗ-ΡοΣ ΕΡΜΑΙοΥ Similar type.	Similar.
20	140·6	Æ 1·1		to l., ✠; to r., ⬚ ς. [Pl. xv. 4.]
21	144·6	Æ 1·		„ ✠; „ ∪.
22	34·9	Æ ·65		to l., ⬓; to r., ⊠.
23	29·4	Æ ·65		„ ⬗.
			ΒΑΣΙΛΕΩΣ ΣΩΤΗ-ΡΟΣ ΕΡΜΑΙΟΥ Bust of the king r., diad. and helmeted.	Similar.
24	37·7	Æ ·65		to l., ✠. [Pl. xv. 5.]

No.	Wt.	Metal. Size.	Obverse.	Reverse.
			(β) Bronze; round; with portrait.	
			ΒΑΣΙΛΕΩΣ ΣΩΤΗΡΟΣ ΕΡΜΑΙΟΥ Bust of the king r., diad.	[Kharoshthi legend] (*Maharajasa tradatasa Heramayasa*). Zeus, laur., seated l. on throne with back; his r. hand advanced; in his l., sceptre.
25		Æ ·95		to l., [monogram]; to r., Ƶ.
26		Æ 1·		„ „ , uncertain Indian letter. [I. O. C. Pl. xv. 6.]
27		Æ ·95		„ „ „ uncertain Indian letter.
28		Æ ·85		„ „ „ Ƭ. [I. O. C.]
29		Æ ·95		„ „ „ uncertain Indian letter.
30		Æ ·9		„ „ „ Ψ. [I. O. C.]
31		Æ ·95		„ „ „ ♈.
32		Æ 1·05		„ „ „ „
33		Æ 1·		„ „ „ ℏ.
34		Æ ·95		„ „ „ „
35		Æ ·95		„ „ „ Ψ.
36		Æ 1·		„ „ „ ϛ. [I. O. C.]
37		Æ ·95		„ ⊠; „ ∾.

No.	Wt.	Metal. Size.	Obverse.	Reverse.
			ΒΑΣΙΛΕΩΣ ΣΩΤΗ- **ΡοΣ ΕΡΜΑΙοΥ** Bust of the king r., diad.	𐨤𐨫𐨂𐨪𐨗 𐨤𐨟𐨿𐨪𐨡 𐨱𐨅𐨪𐨨𐨪𐨽 (*Maharajasa tradatasa Heramayasa*). Zeus, laur., seated l. on throne with back; his r. hand advanced; in his l., sceptre.
38		Æ ·9		to l., ⊠; to r., 𐨪. [I. O. C.]
39		Æ ·9		„ „ „ 𐨤·.
40		Æ ·9		„ „ „ 7·. „
41		Æ ·6		to l., ⊕; to r., Ϙ·.
42		Æ ·6		„ „ „ 7·. [I. O. C.]
43		Æ ·7		„ „ „ 𐨪·. [Pl. xv. 7.]
44		Æ ·6		„ ⊠; „ 𐨪·. [I. O. C.]

(γ) *Bronze; round;* **ΣΥ** *inserted after* **Σ[Ω]ΤΗΡοΣ.***

No.	Wt.	Metal. Size.	Obverse.	Reverse.
			ΒΑΣΙΛΕΩΣ ΣΤΗ- **ΡοΣ ΣΥ ΕΡΜΑΙοΥ** Bust of the king r., diad.	𐨤𐨫𐨂𐨪𐨗 𐨤𐨱𐨟𐨅𐨪𐨨𐨪𐨽 (*Maharajasa mahatasa Heramayasa*). Type as last, degraded.
45		Æ ·8		to l., (?); to r., ⊠.
46		Æ ·7		„ 𝕃 „
47		Æ ·8		„ „ „
48		Æ ·75		„ „ „
			Similar.	Inscr. various. Nike l.; holds wreath and palm.
49		Æ ·65		inscr. 𐨤𐨩𐨪𐨩𐨪 𐨤𐨩𐨪~[𐨂. to r., ⊠.
50		Æ ·6	(obscure).	„ ~𐨂𐨤𐨫𐨪~𐨂. to l., ✝; to r., ⊠.

* Other coins with the same obverse inscription and type, but bearing on the reverse the name of Kadphises and the type of Herakles, are described among the coins of Kadphises I., below.

No.	Wt.	Metal. Size.	Obverse.	Reverse.
			(δ) *Bronze; square; without portrait.*	
			ΒΑΣΙΛΕΩΣ ΣΩΤΗ-ΡΟΣ ΕΡΜΑΙΟΥ Bearded male bust r., radiate, wearing Phrygian cap.	ᵖᴧᴜᴸᵏ ᵖᵞᶾᶘ ᵖᵞᵞ·ᴺᵞ (*Māhārajasa tradatasa Heramayasa*). Horse r., trotting.
51		Æ ·8		below, 🜚.
52		Æ ·75		„ „
53		Æ ·75		„ ⊕. [I. O. C.]
54		Æ ·75		„ „ „
55		Æ ·75		„ „ [I. O. C. Pl. xv. 8.]

HERMAEUS AND CALLIOPE.

(a) *Silver.*

No.	Wt.	Metal. Size.	Obverse.	Reverse.
			ΒΑΣΙΛΕΩΣ ΣΩΤΗ-ΡΟΣ ΕΡΜΑΙΟΥ ΚΑΙ ΚΑΛΛΙΟΠΗΣ Busts jugate r. of the King and Queen, both diad.	ᵖᴧᴜᴸᵏ ᵖᵞᶾᶘ ᵖᵞᵞᴺᵥ ᴧʰᴧᴴᶄ (*Maharajasa tradatasa Heramayasa Kaliyapaya*). King, helmeted and diad., r. on horseback; horse prancing, bow and lance on his back.
1	36·2	Æ ·65		below, 🜚. [Pl. xv. 9.]
2	33·2	Æ ·6		„ „ [I. O. C. Pl. xv. 10.]

No.	Wt.	Metal. Size.	Obverse.	Reverse.
				RANJABALA.
				(a) *Silver.*
			BACIΛEI BACIΛE-ωC CωTHPOC PAΙY Bust of the king r., diad.	ⱅⱜⱨⱨⱜⱨⱜⱨⱨ (*Apratihata-chakrasa chhatrapasa Rajabulasa*). Pallas l.; holding in l. hand aegis, and with r., hurling thunderbolt.
1	38·	Æ ·55		to l., ⱨ; to r., ⱨ. [Pl. xv. 11.]
			Blundered inscr. Same type.	ⱅⱜⱨ ... ⱜⱨ ⱅⱨZⱨ (*Chha-trapasa Apra ... chakrasa Rajabulasa*). Same type.
2	36·8	Æ ·55		to l., ⱨ; to r., .∼. [Pl. xv. 12.]
3	36·6	Æ ·55	(both sides blundered).	„ „ „ „
4	36·4	Æ ·55	(inscr. **BA MOC-CωTHPOCPA**).	„ „ „ „
5	36·	Æ ·55		„ „ (name, „ ⱅⱨⱨⱨ *Ramja-bulasa*).
6	30·8	Æ ·55		„ ∼; „ ⱨ Ɛ̇.
7	35·7	Æ ·5		„ ⱨ; „ ⱀ. (Inscr., ... ⱅⱨZⱨ∼ᴗ *mahachhatrapasa*, &c.)
8	35·8	Æ ·5		„ ∼; „ ⱝ. „

No.	Wt.	Metal. Size.	Obverse.	Reverse.

MAUES.

(a) Bronze; round; Greek legend only.

			Head of elephant r. ; bell round neck.	**ΒΑΣΙΛΕΩΣ** Caduceus. **ΜΑΥΟΥ**
1		Æ 1·15		to l., 𝍊. [I. O. C. Pl. xvi. 1.]
2		Æ 1·15		„ „

(β) Silver; type, Zeus.

			ΒΑΣΙΛΕΩΣ ΒΑΣΙ-ΛΕΩΝ ΜΕΓΑΛΟΥ ΜΑΥΟΥ Zeus standing l., clad in himation; r. hand extended; in l., long sceptre.	ꤔꤙ~꤅ ꤔꤛꤏꤡꤛꤏ (Rajadi-ꤔ ꤏꤙ rajasa mahatasa Moasa). Nike r.; holds wreath and palm bound with fillet.
3	151·	Æ 1·15		to r., ⊞. [Pl. xvi. 2.]

(γ) Bronze; round; type, King on horseback.

			ΒΑΣΙΛΕΩΣ ΒΑΣΙ-ΛΕΩΝ ΜΕΓΑ[ΛΟΥ [ΜΑΥΟΥ?] King r. on horseback; whip over shoulder; lance couched.	ꤏꤙ ꤔꤙ~꤅ ꤔꤛꤏꤡꤛꤏ (Rajadirajasa mahatasa Moasa). Female figure, facing, diad.; holds in r. hand, patera, containing offerings; l. rests on wheel; on head, turreted crown. (Tyche).
4		Æ 1·2	to r., ⧖.	to l., ΨϚ. [Pl. xvi. 3.]

No.	Wt.	Metal. Size.	Obverse.	Reverse.
			(δ) Bronze ; round ; other types.	
			ΒΑΣΙΛΕΩΣ ΒΑΣΙ-ΛΕΩΝ ΜΕΓΑΛΟΥ ΜΑΥΟΥ Artemis running r., radiate, with veil floating round her head ; clad in short chiton and boots.	↑ꟼ〜∪ ꟼꓬꓶ⅄ꓶꟼ (*Rajadi-* ꟼ ?⅄ *rajasa mahatasa Moasa*). Indian humped bull l.
5	Æ 1·			to l., 𝒜 . [Pl. XVI. 4.]
6	Æ 1·			„ „
7	Æ 1·			„ 𝐍 .
			Same inscr. Herakles, facing ; holds in l., club and lion's skin.	Same inscr. Maneless lion l.
8	Æ 1·05			to l., 𝐍 . [Pl. XVI. 5.]
			(ε) Bronze ; square ; type, King on horseback.	
			ΒΑΣΙΛΕΩΣ ΒΑΣΙ-ΛΕΩΝ ΜΕΓΑΛΟΥ ΜΑΥΟΥ King r. on horseback ; whip over shoulder ; r. hand advanced.	ꟼ〜∪ ꟼꓬꓶ⅄ꓶꟼ (*Rajadi-* ꟼ ?⅄ *rajasa mahatasa Moasa*). Pallas r., her garment flying ; holds in l. hand, spear and shield ; r. extended ; before her, altar.
9	Æ ·9			to r., Ψꙅ . [Pl. XVI. 6.]
			Same inscr. King r. on horseback ; whip over shoulder ; lance couched.	Same inscr. Nike l. ; holds wreath and palm.
10	Æ 1·			to l., 𝐍 . [Pl. XVI. 7.]

No.	Wt.	Metal. Size.	Obverse.	Reverse.
			(ζ) *Bronze; square; other types.*	
11		Æ ·95	ΒΑΣΙΛΕΩΣ ΒΑΣΙΛΕΩΝ ΜΕΓΑΛΟΥ ΜΑΥΟΥ Draped female figure facing, holds sceptre transversely; on her head, crescent; and on either side, star.	𐨤𐨩𐨪 𐨤𐨿.∿∪ 𐨤𐨩𐨪𐨪𐨩𐨿 (*Rajadirajasa mahātasa Moasa*). Nike l.; holds wreath and palm. to l., A̲T̲. [Pl. xvi. 8.]
12		Æ 1·	Same inscr. Zeus, laur., seated l. on throne; holds in l. hand sceptre; r. extended towards small winged female figure, who seems to be an embodiment of the thunderbolt.	Same inscr. Female figure, facing, wearing turreted crown and holding long sceptre; holds out in r. hand her veil. (Tyche). to l., A̲T̲. [Pl. xvi. 9.]
13		Æ ·9		„ „
14		Æ 1·1	Same inscr. Zeus, seated l. on throne; holds in r. hand Nike, who carries wreath and palm; before him, forepart of elephant r., with trunk raised.	Same inscr. Herakles, facing; holds in l. hand, club and lion's skin; with r., crowns himself ?
15		Æ ·95	Same inscr. Poseidon l., clad in himation; r. hand on hip; in l., trident; r. foot placed on shoulder of a river-god.	Same inscr. Female figure, clad in chiton and himation, facing; stands between two vines. (Maenad ?). to l., A̲T̲. [I. O. C. Pl. xvii. 1.]
16		Æ ·9	(Poseidon raises r. hand); to r., ⋈.	[I. O. C.]

No.	Wt.	Metal. Size.	Obverse.	Reverse.
17		Æ ·9	ΒΑΣΙΛΕΩΣ ΒΑΣΙ-ΛΕΩΝ ΜΕΓΑΛΟΥ ΜΑΥΟΥ Poseidon striding l., hurling thunderbolt to r., and holding in left hand aplustre; beside him, river-god, leaping up.	𐨪𐨗 𐨪𐨿.~ᴗ 𐨨𐨆𐨀𐨯 (*Rajadirajasa mahātasa Moasa*). Female figure, clad in chiton and himation, facing; stands between two vines. (Maenad ?). to l., ⊠. [I. O. C. Pl. xvii. 2.]
18		Æ 1·1	Same inscr. Male figure l., chlamys flying behind; holds club and trident. to l., ⬟.	Same inscr. Female figure r., peplum flying; holds long fillet. to r., ΨϚ. [I. O. C. Pl. xvii. 3.]
19		Æ 1·05		
20		Æ ·9	Same inscr. Female figure l.; r. hand advanced; in l., cornucopiae. (Tyche ?).	Same inscr. Male figure, facing; clad in himation; r. hand on hip; wears petasus. (Hermes ?). to l., Ꞵ⊤. [Pl. xvii. 4.]
21		Æ ·9	Same inscr. Elephant running r., holds in trunk, wreath: in square of fillet-pattern.	Same inscr. King, facing, seated cross-legged on cushion; sword on his knees: in square of fillet-pattern. to r., ⊠. [Pl. xvii. 5.]
22		Æ ·9		,, ,,
23		Æ ·9		,, ⊠.
24		Æ ·85		,, ,,
25		Æ 1·05	Similar.	Same inscr. Indian humped bull r. to r., ⊠. [Pl. xvii. 6.]

No.	Wt.	Metal. Size.	Obverse.	Reverse.
			ΒΑΣΙΛΕΩΣ ΜΑΥΟΥ Apollo l.; holds in r. hand arrow; in l., bow.	ꓱ ꓶꖴ ꓱꓵꓱ~ꖴ (*Maharajasa Moasa*). Tripod, in square of dots.
26		Æ ·6	to l., Ϻ.	[Pl. xvii. 7.]
27		Æ ·55	„ Ϻ.	
			Same inscr. Horse r, trotting.	Same inscr. Bow in case.
28		Æ ·8		to l, Ϻ.

No.	Wt.	Metal. Size.	Obverse.	Reverse.
				AZES.
				(a) *Silver; type, Zeus.*
			ΒΑΣΙΛΕΩΣ ΒΑΣΙ-ΛΕΩΝ ΜΕΓΑΛΟΥ ΑΖΟΥ The king r., on horseback; holds lance, couched.	𐨦𐨿~υ 𐨤𐨩𐨪𐨩𐨪 𐨤𐨩𐨪~υ 𐨤𐨣𐨿 (*Maharajasa rajarajasa mahātasa Ayasa*). Zeus l., radiate; r. hand advanced; in l., long sceptre.
1	146·5	Æ 1·1	below, 𐨤.	to l., ⊞; to r., 𐨩. [Pl. XVII. 8.]
			Similar.	Same inscr. Zeus, facing, laur.; holds winged thunderbolt and long sceptre.
2	145·7	Æ 1·15		to l., ☒; to r., 𐨛. [I. O. C. Pl. XVII. 9.]
3	150·3	Æ 1·05		„ „ „ „
4	140·6	Æ 1·1	below, 𐨛.	„ Ā; „ 𐨪. [I. O. C.]
5	35·5	Æ ·65		to l., ☒; to r., 𐨛. [I. O. C. Pl. XVII. 10.]
			Similar.	Same inscr. Zeus, facing, laur.; hurls with r., thunderbolt; and holds in l., long sceptre.
6	37·9	Æ ·7	below, Ψ.	to l., Ā̶; to r., 𐨪. [Pl. XVII. 11.]
7	35·	Æ ·65	„ „	„ „ „ „

L

No.	Wt.	Metal. Size.	Obverse.	Reverse.
			ΒΑΣΙΛΕΩΣ ΒΑΣΙ-ΛΕΩΝ ΜΕΓΑΛΟΥ ΑΖΟΥ The king r., on horseback; holds whip.	౼౽.~౿ ౼౽౼౽౼ ౼౽౼~౿ ౼౸౽ (*Maharajasa rajarajasa mahātasa Ayasa*). Zeus l.; holds in r. hand, wreath-bearing Nike; in l., long sceptre.
8	128·	Æ ·95	below, ౽ ·	to l., ⊞; to r., ౼ ·
9	146·7	Æ 1·1	to r., ౽ ·	„ „ „ ౾ ·
10	140·	Æ 1·1	„ ౽ ·	„ „ „ ౾ · ౼
11	136·8	Æ 1·	„ ౾ ·	„ „ „ [I. O. C. Pl. xvii. 12.]
12	142·3	Æ ·95	„ ౽ ·	„ „ „ „
13	149·	Æ 1·1	„ ౺ ·	„ „ „ „
14	136·	Æ ·9	„ ౼ ·	„ ⊞; „ ౾ · ౽
15	150·4	Æ ·9	„ ౼ ·	„ „ „ „ [I. O. C.]
16	128·7	Æ ·95	„ ౽ ·	„ ⊞; „ ౾ · ౽
17	148·7	Æ ·95	„ ౽ ·	„ „ „ ⊡ · ౼
18	149·	Æ ·9	„ ౼ ·	„ ࿔; „ ౽ · ౼
19	147·7	Æ ·95	„ ౽ ·	„ „ „ „ [I. O. C.]
20	147·	Æ ·95	„ ౽ ·	„ ࿔; „ mon. „ ౽

No.	Wt.	Metal. Size.	Obverse.	Reverse.
			ΒΑΣΙΛΕΩΣ ΒΑΣΙΛΕΩΝ ΜΕΓΑΛΟΥ ΑΖΟΥ The king r., on horseback; holds whip.	𐨤𐨱.~𐤖 𐤕𐤗𐤗𐤗𐤗 𐤕𐤗𐤱~𐤖 𐤕𐤠𐤗 (*Maharajasa rajarajasa mahātasa Ayasa*). Zeus l.; holds in r. hand, wreath-bearing Nike; in l., long sceptre.
21	32·9	Æ ·6	to r., Ψ .	to l., 𐤗 ; to r., Ζ . Ⱶ 𐤗
22	28·5	Æ ·6	,, ,,	,, ,, ,, ,,
23	33·3	Æ ·55	,, ᴗ .	,, Ⱶ ; ,, Ⴑ .
24	34·8	Æ ·6	,, 𐤎 .	,, ,, ,, [I. O. C. Pl. XVII. 13.]
25	30·	Æ ·6	,, 𐤗 . (inverted).	,, Ⱶ ; ,, ,,
26	36·5	Æ ·6	,, 𐤗 .	,, ,, ,, ,,
27	37·	Æ ·6	,, ,,	,, ,, ,, ,,
28	35·6	Æ ·6	,, 𐤓 .	,, ,, ,, ⸞ 𐤗 . [I. O. C.]
29	36·8	Æ ·6	,, Ϛ .	,, ,, ,, 𐤓 .
30	33·5	Æ ·55	,, Ƶ .	,, Ⱶ ; ,, uncertain letter.
31	27·4	Æ ·6	,, 𐤗 .	,, ,, ,, Ϛ . [I. O. C.]
32	33·9	Æ ·6	,, 𐤎 .	,, Σ ; ,, Ⱶ 𐤓 .
33	34·	Æ 65	,, 𐤓 .	,, Ⱶ ; ,, mon. Ζ .
34	30·5	Æ ·6	,, ,,	,, ,, ,, ,, ,, [I. O. C.]

No.	Wt.	Metal. Size.	Obverse.	Reverse.
			ΒΑΣΙΛΕΩΣ ΒΑΣΙ-ΛΕΩΝ ΜΕΓΑΛΟΥ ΑΖΟΥ The king r., on horseback; holds whip.	𐨤𐨪~𐨜 𐨤𐨩𐨪𐨝𐨩 𐨤𐨩𐨪~𐨜 𐨤𐨙𐨩 (*Maharajasa rajarajasa mahātasa Ayasa*). Zeus l.; holds in r. hand, wreath-bearing Nike; in l., long sceptre.
35	31·	Æ ·65	to r., Ψ.	to l., ✠; to r., ☒ 𐨛.
36	36·4	Æ ·6	„ 𐨤.	„ „ „ „ „
37	36·2	Æ ·6	„ 𐨥.	„ „ „ 𐨛.
38	37·2	Æ ·6	„ 𐨤.	„ „ „ A 𐨛.
39	32·9	Æ ·6	„ 𐨣.	„ „ „ „ „
40	35·8	Æ ·6	„ 𐨤.	„ „ „ O „
41	30·2	Æ ·5	„ 𐨢.	„ „ „ „ 𐨤. [I. O. C.]
42	31·	Æ ·55	„ 𐨞.	„ „ „ Δ M. 𐨥 „
43	33·	Æ ·6	„ 𐨙.	„ „ „ B 𐨛.
44	28·7	Æ ·6	„ 𐨤.	„ „ „ „ „
45	22·6	Æ ·6	„ ∪.	„ „ „ „ „
46	35·3	Æ ·6	„ 𐨥.	„ „ „ „ Σ.
47	35·2	Æ ·6	„ 𐨞.	„ „ „ „ 𐨥.
48	37·2	Æ ·6	„ 𐨟.	„ „ „ „ „ [I. O. C.]

No.	Wt.	Metal. Size.	Obverse.	Reverse.
			ΒΑΣΙΛΕΩΣ ΒΑΣΙ-ΛΕΩΝ ΜΕΓΑΛΟΥ ΑΖΟΥ The king r., on horseback; holds whip.	𐤐𐤓.~𐤅 𐤐𐤚𐤓𐤚𐤓 𐤐𐤚𐤓~𐤅 𐤐𐤀𐤆 (*Maharajasa rajarajasa mahātasa Ayasa*). Zeus l.; holds in r. hand, wreath-bearing Nike; in l., long sceptre.
49	32·	Æ ·55	to r., *h*.	to l., 🏵; to r., Ʒ.
50	34·8	Æ ·55	„ Ψ.	„ „ „ 𝟕.
51	35·5	Æ ·55	„ uncertain letter.	„ „ „ ∈. 𝟃
52	34·3	Æ ·55	„ „	„ „ „ „
53	27·5	Æ ·6	„ 𝟃.	„ „ „ 𐠦. [I. O. C.]
54	32·	Æ ·6	„ 𝟃 𝟕.	„ „ „ „ „

[Most of the above coins are of base metal and very rude execution. In nos. 16 and 46 the inscr. reads *rajadirajasa*].

(β) *Silver; type, Poseidon.*

			ΒΑΣΙΛΕΩΣ ΒΑΣΙ-ΛΕΩΝ ΜΕΓΑΛΟΥ ΑΖΟΥ King r., on horseback; holds whip.	𐤐𐤓.~𐤅 𐤐𐤚𐤓𐤚𐤓 𐤐𐤚𐤓~𐤅 𐤐𐤀𐤆 (*Maharajasa rajarajasa mahātasa Ayasa*). Poseidon r.; holds in l. hand, trident.
55	138·	Æ ·95	to r., 𝟃.	to l., 🏵; to r., 𝟃. [Pl. XVIII. 1.]

No.	Wt.	Metal. Size.	Obverse.	Reverse.
				(γ) *Silver; type, Pallas.*
			ΒΑΣΙΛΕΩΣ ΒΑΣΙΛΕΩΝ ΜΕΓΑΛΟΥ ΑΖΟΥ King r., on horseback; holds lance, couched.	ΡʔჍ Ρɤʔⴽ⅁ ΡɤʔჍ Ρ∧ʔ (*Maharajasa rajarajasa mahātasa Ayasa*). Pallas l.; in raised r. hand, thunderbolt; l. holds shield.
56	145·8	Æ ·95	to r., ⅄.	to l., Ʌ̄; to r., ʔ. [Pl. xviii. 2.]
57	132·6	Æ 1· (plated)	in ex., ʔ.	„　„　„　„
58	145·5	Æ 1·05	to r., ʔ.	„　„　„　Ⱡ.
59	145·5	Æ ·95		„　„　„　„
60	139·8	Æ 1·	„　Ϙ.	„　„　„　„
61	147·	Æ 1·	„　⅄.	„　„　„　„　[I. O. C.]
62	32·8	Æ ·65	to r., ʔ.	to l., Ʌ̄; to r., Ⱡ.
63	29·6	Æ ·7	„　⅄.	„　„　„　„　[Pl. xviii. 3.]
64	37·5	Æ ·65	„　ʔ.	„　„　„　„
65	35·	Æ ·6	„　Ϙ.	„　„　„　„
66	36·5	Æ ·7	„　⅄.	„　„　„　„
67	35·	Æ ·7	„　„	„　„　„　„
68	36·7	Æ ·65	„　∿.	„　„　„　ʔ.
69	34·1	Æ ·6	„　„	„　„　„　„　[I. O. C.]

No.	Wt.	Metal. Size.	Obverse.	Reverse.
			ΒΑΣΙΛΕΩΣ ΒΑΣΙ-ΛΕΩΝ ΜΕΓΑΛ Υ ΑΖΟΥ King r., on horseback; holds whip.	𐨤𐨿𐨪 𐨫 𐨤𐨩𐨪𐨫𐨿𐨪 𐨤𐨩𐨪𐨫 𐨤𐨫𐨿 (*Maharajasa rajarajasa mahātasa Ayasa*). Pallas, facing; holds in l. hand, spear and shield; with r., crowns herself.
70	138·5	Æ 1·	to r., 𐨤 .	to l., ⌗; to r., ◻ . [Pl. xviii. 4.]
71	35·	Æ ·6	to r., 𐨤 .	to l., ⌗; to r., 𐨀 .
72	34·5	Æ ·65	„ „	„ „ „ „ [Pl. xviii. 5.]
73	38·	Æ ·65	„ Ψ .	„ „ „ „
74	38·	Æ ·65	„ 𐨤 .	„ „ „ „
75	36·4	Æ ·6	„ 𐨤 .	„ „ „ „
76	36·	Æ ·65	„ 𐨤 .	„ „ „ ◻ .
77	39·	Æ ·65	„ „	„ „ „ „
78	37·6	Æ ·65	„ 𐨤 .	„ „ „ „
79	38·7	Æ ·65	„ „	„ „ „ „
80	36·9	Æ ·6	„ 𐨤 .	„ „ „ „
81	36·3	Æ ·65	„ „	„ „ „ „
82	34·5	Æ ·65	„ 𐨤 .	„ „ „ „ [I. O. C.]

No.	Wt.	Metal. Size.	Obverse.	Reverse.
			ΒΑΣΙΛΕΩΣ ΒΑΣΙΛΕΩΝ ΜΕΓΑΛΟΥ ΑΖΟΥ King r., on horseback; holds whip.	ᚹ∿ᚹ ᚹᚹᚹ ᚹᚹ∿ ᚹᚹᚹ (*Maharajasa rajarajasa mahātasa Ayasa*). Pallas, facing; holds in l. hand, spear and shield; with r., crowns herself.
83	30·6	Æ ·55	to r., letter.	to l., ⚏; to r., ⊠.
84	35·3	Æ ·65	„ 𐤀.	„ 𐤉; „ 𐤀.
85	33·6	Æ ·65	„ „	„ „ „ „
86	36·8	Æ ·65	„ 𐤒.	„ „ „ „
			Similar.	Same inscr. Pallas, standing l.; r. hand advanced; in l., shield.
87	34·1	Æ ·7	to r., 𐤀.	to l., 𐤉; to r., 𐤀.
88	36·6	Æ ·6	„ 𐤓.	„ „ „ 𐤀. [Pl. xviii. 6.]
			Similar.	Same inscr. Pallas, facing; holds in r. hand, spear; shield slung over back.
89	33·6	Æ ·6	to r., 𐤅.	to l., 𐤇; to r., 𐤔. [Pl. xviii. 7.]

No.	Wt.	Metal. Size.	Obverse.	Reverse.
			ΒΑΣΙΛΕΩΣ ΒΑΣΙ-ΛΕΩΝ ΜΕΓΑΛοΥ ΑΖοV King r., on horseback; holds whip.	ꖡꖗ~ꖴ ꖡꖗꖗꖡꖗ ꖡꖗꖗ~ꖴ ꖡꖥ? (*Maharajasa rajarajasa mahatasa Ayasa*). Pallas r.; her r. hand advanced; in her l., spear and shield.
90	144·8	Æ ·95	to r., ⅍.	to l., 🝙; to r., 🜨. [Pl. xviii. 8.]
91	146·7	Æ ·95	„ ꖘ.	„ 🀫; „ 🀭. (inscr. *rajadirajasa*).
92	140·5	Æ ·95	„ ꖕ.	„ 🀪; „ ꖖ.
93	146·7	Æ ·95	„ „	„ „ „ 🀯. (inscr. *rajadirajasa*).
94	130·5	Æ 1·	„ ꖡ.	„ Φ 🁢; „ 🀮.
95	123·8	Æ1·05	„ ꖑ.	„ 🁣; „ 🀫.
96	140·2	Æ 1·	„ ꖡ.	„ Α 🁢; „ 🀪. [I. O. C.] (inscr. *rajadirajasa*).
97	147·8	Æ ·95	„ ꖢ.	„ „ ⅍; „ 🀯. [I. O. C.]
98	143·5	Æ ·95	„ ꖤ.	„ „ „ „ „ „
99	142·8	Æ ·95	„ ꖧ.	„ „ „ „ „ „
100	147·3	Æ ·95	„ ꖗ; below, uncertain letter.	„ 🜨; „ 🀮. (inscr. *rajadirajasa*).
101	147·	Æ ·95	„ „	„ „ „ „ „
102	152·9	Æ ·9	„ „	„ „ „ „ „
103	141·4	Æ ·85	„ ꖦ.	„ „ 🁢; „ „ „
104	118·7	Æ ·9	„ ꖨ.	„ „ „ „ „

M

No.	Wt.	Metal. Size.	Obverse.	Reverse.
			ΒΑΣΙΛΕΩΣ ΒΑΣΙ-ΛΕΩΝ ΜΕΓΑΛΟΥ ΑΖοΥ King r., on horseback; holds whip.	꠸꠸꠸ ꠸꠸꠸꠸ ꠸꠸꠸ ꠸꠸꠸ (*Maharajasa rajarajasa mahatasa Ayasa*). Pallas r.; her r. hand advanced; in her l., spear and shield.
105	37·6	Æ ·6	to r., ꠸.	to l., ⊠; to r., ⌸.
106	36·7	Æ ·65	„ ꠸.	„ „ „ „
107	35·6	Æ ·65		„ „ „ „ [Pl. xviii. 9.]
108	28·5	Æ ·6	„ uncertain letter.	„ ☒; „ ⌸. [I. O. C.]

(δ) *Silver; type, City?*

No.	Wt.	Metal. Size.	Obverse.	Reverse.
			ΒΑΣΙΛΕΩΣ ΒΑΣΙ-ΛΕΩΝ ΜΕΓΑΛΟΥ ΑΖοΥ King r., on horseback; holds lance, couched.	꠸꠸꠸ ꠸꠸꠸꠸ ꠸꠸꠸ ꠸꠸꠸ (*Maharajasa rajarajasa mahatasa Ayasa*). A City? l.; holds in r. hand, object resembling a brazier; in l., palm bound with fillet.
109	136·5	Æ1·05	to r., Ζ.	to l., ⊞; to r., ꠸. [Pl. xviii. 10.]
110	143·	Æ 1·	„ ꠸.	„ „ „ „
111	34·3	Æ ·7		to l., ꠸ ꠸; to r., Ζ. [Pl xviii. 11.]

No.	Wt.	Metal. Size.	Obverse.	Reverse.
			(ε) *Silver ; without figure of King.*	
			ΒΑΣΙΛΕΩΣ ΒΑΣΙ-ΛΕΩΝ ΜΕΓΑΛΟΥ ΑΖΟΥ Zeus l., laur.; r. hand advanced ; in l., sceptre held transversely.	Ƥ٦.~ᴗ ƤYꞀYꞀ ƤYꞀ~ᴗ Ƥ∧? (*Maharajasa rajarajasa mahātasa Ayasa*). Nike r., winged ; holds wreath and palm bound with fillet.
112	35·5	Æ ·7		to r., ◹. [Pl. xviii. 12.]
113	35·1	Æ ·7		„ „
114	36·7	Æ ·7		„ „ [I. O. C.]
			(ζ) *Bronze; type, King, seated.*	
			ΒΑΣΙΛΕΩΣ ΒΑΣΙ-ΛΕΩΝ ΜΕΓΑΛΟΥ ΑΖΟΥ King, facing, seated cross-legged on cushion ; holds in r. hand, ankus ; in l., sword, which rests on his knees.	Ƥ٦~ᴗ ƤYꞀYꞀ ƤYꞀ~ᴗ Ƥ∧? (*Maharajasa rajarajasa mahatasa Ayasa*). Hermes l., with chlamys flying; r. hand raised ; in l., caduceus.
115		Æ 1·	to l., ⳨.	to l., ᙄ; to r., Ϛ.
116		Æ 1·05	„ „	„ ∷ „ „ [I. O. C. Pl. xix. 1.]
117		Æ ·95	„ ⳴.	„ „ „ „
118		Æ 1·05	„ „	„ ᙄ.
119		Æ 1·	„ „	„ ⊞; „ Ꞁ.
120		Æ 1·		„ „ „ „

No.	Wt.	Metal. Size.	Obverse.	Reverse.
			ΒΑΣΙΛΕΩΣ ΒΑΣΙΛΕΩΝ ΜΕΓΑΛΟΥ ΑΖΟΥ King, facing, seated cross-legged on cushion; holds in r. hand, ankus; in l., sword, which rests on his knees.	ꓑꓶ∼ꖌ ꓑꓨꓶꓨꓶ ꓑꓨꓶ∼ꖌ ꓑ∧ꓢ (*Maharajasa rajarajasa mahatasa Ayasa*). Hermes l., with chlamys flying; r. hand raised; in l., caduceus.
121	Æ 1·05		to l., 𐤊.	to l., ⊞; to r., ꓶ.
122	Æ ·95		„ uncertain letter.	„ „ „ Η Ζ. (*inscr. rajadirajasa*).
123	Æ ·95		„ ᗐ.	„ ⊞; „ ᗷ ꓘ.
124	Æ ·7			„ „ „ „
125	Æ 1·		„ ⅄ (inverted).	„ Ⱳ; „ ꓵ. (*inscr. rajadirajasa*).
126	Æ ·9		„ ᗐ.	„ ⨁ ⱱ; „ ꓑ ꓶ.

(η) *Bronze; type, Demeter or City.*

No.	Wt.	Metal. Size.	Obverse.	Reverse.
			ΒΑΣΙΛΕΩΣ ΒΑΣΙΛΕΩΝ ΜΕΓΑΛΟΥ ΑΖΟΥ Demeter? seated l. on throne, modius on head; r. hand raised; in l., cornucopiae.	ꓑꓶ∼ꖌ ꓑꓨꓶꓨꓶ ꓑꓨꓶ∼ꖌ ꓑ∧ꓢ (*Maharajasu rajarajasa mahatasa Ayasa*). Hermes l.; r. hand raised; in l., caduceus.
127	Æ 1·05			to l., ⱶ; to r., ⊠.
128	Æ 1·05			„ „ „ „
129	Æ 1·05			„ „ „ „ (restruck). [I. O. C. Pl. xix. 2.]
130	Æ 1·			„ „ „ „ [I. O. C.]
131	Æ 1·			„ „ „ „ „
132	Æ 1·1			„ „

[Restruck on a coin of Azes, cl. κ; types, elephant, humped bull]].

No.	Wt.	Metal. Size.	Obverse.	Reverse.
			ΒΑΣΙΛΕΩΣ ΒΑΣΙΛΕΩΝ ΜΕΓΑΛΟΥ ΑΖΟΥ Hermes l., wears chlamys; r. hand advanced; in l., caduceus.	Ϙϩ~υ Ϙϒϡϒϡ Ϙϒϡ~υ ϘΛϡ (*Maharajasa rajarajasa mahatasa Ayasa*). Demeter? standing l., wears modius; r. hand advanced; in l., cornucopiae.
133		Æ ·75	to l., 𝔐 .	to l., ✠; to r., ϙ [Pl. xix. 3.]
			Same inscr. Lion r.	Similar.
134		Æ ·75		to l., ✠; to r., ϡ .
135		Æ ·65	above, ϑ .	„ „ „ Є ϡ. [Pl. xix. 4.]
136		Æ ·65	„ „	„ „ „ o ϡ .

(θ) *Bronze ; type, male deity.*

No.	Wt.	Metal. Size.	Obverse.	Reverse.
			ΒΑΣΙΛΕΩΣ ΒΑΣΙΛΕΩΝ ΜΕΓΑΛΟΥ ΑΖΟΥ Female deity, facing, clad in himation; holds in raised r. hand, flower; stands on lotus; beside her, lion? (Lakshmí?).	Ϙϩ~υ Ϙϒϡϒϡ Ϙϒϡ~υ ϘΛϡ (*Maharajasa rajarajasa mahatasa Ayasa*). Humped bull r.
137		Æ 1·	to l., ⚓ .	to r., Ƶ . [Pl xix. 5.]

(ι) *Bronze ; types, lion and bull.*

No.	Wt.	Metal. Size.	Obverse.	Reverse.
			ΒΑΣΙΛΕΩΣ ΒΑΣΙΛΕΩΝ ΜΕΓΑΛΟΥ ΑΖΟΥ Humped Indian bull r.	Ϙϩ~υ Ϙϒϡϡϡ Ϙϒϡ~υ ϘΛϡ (*Maharajasa rajadirajasa mahatasa Ayasa*). Lion r.
138		Æ 1·1	above, Ꞧ .	above, ⚠ .
139		Æ 1·1	„ „	„ „

No.	Wt.	Metal. Size.	Obverse.	Reverse.
			ΒΑΣΙΛΕΩΣ ΒΑΣΙΛΕΩΝ ΜΕΓΑΛΟΥ ΑΖΟΥ Humped Indian bull r.	ᚃᚔ᛫᛫᛫ (Maharajasa rajadirajasa mahatasa Ayasa). Lion r.
140	Æ 1·1		above, 𐊇.	above, 𐊐.
141	Æ 1·		„ 𐊈.	„ 𐊐.
142	Æ 1·1		„ 𐊀; to r., 𐊝.	„ 𐊉
143	Æ 1·05		„ 𐊉; „ 𐊟.	„ 𐊗.
144	Æ 1·05		„ „ „ 𐊝.	„ „
145	Æ 1·		„ „ „ 𐊜.	„ „
146	Æ 1·1		„ „ „ 𐊝.	„ 𐊐.
147	Æ ·95		„ „	„ 𐊗. [I. O. C.]
148	Æ 1·		„ 𐊟.	„ 𐊒.
149	Æ 1·1		„ 𐊇.	„ 𐊓.
150	Æ 1·2		„ „ „ 𐊏.	„ „
151	Æ 1·1		„ 𐊇; „ „	„ 𐊒.
152	Æ 1·2		„ 𐊇; „ 𐊞.	„ 𐊓. [Pl. xix. 6.]
153	Æ 1·1		„ „ „ 𐊜.	„ 𐊐.
154	Æ ·85		„ 𐊀.	„ 𐊉.
155	Æ ·85		„ 𐊅; „ 𐊝. (inscription barbarous).	to r., 𐊏.
156	Æ ·8		„ 𐊉.	above, 𐊗. [I. O. C.]

No.	Wt.	Metal. Size.	Obverse.	Reverse.
			(κ) *Bronze ; types, elephant and bull.*	
			ΒΑΣΙΛΕΩΣ ΒΑΣΙ-ΛΕΩΝ ΜΕΓΑΛοΥ ΑΖοΥ Elephant r.	ᘏᒐᐰᐂ ᘏᒐᘁᕽᒐᘁ ᘏᒐᘁᐂ ᘏᐧᘁ (*Maharajasa rajadirajasa mahatasa Ayasa*). Humped bull r.
157	Æ 1·		above, **A**.	above, uncertain letter.
158	Æ ·95		„ „	„ „ •
159	Æ 1·		„ **r̨**.	„ **ᘗ ?**. (inscr. *rajarajasa*).
160	Æ 1·05		„ **?**.	„ „ „ [I. O. C.” Pl. xıx. 7.]
161	Æ 1·		„ **ħ**.	„ **ᕑ ᕶ̨**. (inscr. *rajarajasa*).
162	Æ 1·		„ **?**.	„ „ „ „ [I. O. C.]
163	Æ ·95		„ „	„ **ᕑ ?**. „
164	Æ 1·1		„ **r̨**.	„ „ „ „ „
165	Æ 1·05		„ **?**.	„ „ „ „ „
166	Æ 1·05		„ „	„ „ **ᕶᑫ**. „
167	Æ 1·05		„ „	„ „ **ᕶᕶ̨**. „
168	Æ 1·05			„ „ **ᕶᑫ**.
169	Æ ·75		(inscriptions obscure).	[I. O. C.]
			[In several of the above coins the king's name is misspelt, and appears as **AOZY**, **AOZZY**, **AZOY**, and so forth.]	

No.	Wt.	Metal. Size.	Obverse.	Reverse.
			(λ) *Bronze ; square ; type, King on horseback.*	
			ΒΑΣΙΛΕΩΣ ΒΑΣΙΛΕΩΝ ΜΕΓΑΛΟΥ ΑΖΟΥ The king r., on horseback ; holds in r. hand, lance, couched.	௴௮~௴ ௴௴௴ ௴௴~௴ ௴௴௴ (*Maharajasa rajarajasa mahatasa Ayasa*). Humped bull r.
170	Æ ·95			above, 𝕏 ௴.
171	Æ ·85			„ „ „ (restruck).
172	Æ 1·			„ „ 𝍏. [I. O. C. Pl. xix. 8.]
173	Æ ·95			„ ▣ ; to r., ⟁.
174	Æ ·1	(inscr. barbarous).		„ „
175	Æ ·9		to r., **B** .	„ ⊕ ℎᵗ .
176	Æ ·85		„ „	„ „ ⅄ .
177	Æ 1·			„ 𝕏 ௴.
			(μ) *Bronze ; square ; type, King on camel.*	
			ΒΑΣΙΛΕΩΣ ΒΑΣΙΛΕΩΝ ΜΕΓΑΛΟΥ ΑΖΟΥ King r., seated on camel ; holds whip.	௴௮~௴ ௴௴௴ ௴௴~௴ ௴௴௴ (*Maharajasa rajarajasa mahatasa Ayasa*). Humped bull r.
178	Æ 1·			to r., 𝕏 .
179	Æ 1·			„ „ [I. O. C.]
180	Æ ·85			[Pl. xix. 9.]

No.	Wt.	Metal. Size.	Obverse.	Reverse.
			(ν) *Bronze; square; type, Poseidon.*	
			ΒΑΣΙΛΕΩΣ ΒΑΣΙ-ΛΕΩΝ ΜΕΓΑΛΟΥ ΑΖΟΥ Poseidon l., clad in himation; r. hand on hip; in l., trident; foot placed on shoulder of river-god.	ᛣᚱ.~ᴗ ᚣᛯᚱᛯᚱ ᚣᛯᚱ~ᴗ ᛣᚠᚱ (*Maharajasà rajarajasa mahātasa Ayasa*). Female figure, clad in chiton and himation, facing; holds in each hand, long vine-branch.
181		Æ 1·		to l., 𝔅. [Pl. xix. 10.]
182		Æ 1·		„ „
183		Æ 1·		„ „ [I. O. C.]
184*		Æ 1·2		„ „
			Same inscr. Male figure l., chlamys flying behind; holds club and trident.	Same inscr. Female figure r., peplum flying; holds long fillet.
185		Æ ·8		to r., 𝔅.
			(ξ) *Bronze; square; animal types.*	
			ΒΑΣΙΛΕΩΣ ΒΑΣΙ-ΛΕΩΝ ΜΕΓΑΛΟΥ ΑΖΟΥ Herakles, facing; holds in l. hand, club and lion's skin; and with r., crowns himself.	ᛣᚱ~ᴗ ᚣᛯᚱᛯᚱ ᚣᛯᚱ~ᴗ ᛣᚠᚱ (*Maharajasa rajarajasa mahatasa Ayasa*). Horse r.
186		Æ ·9		above, Ψ.
187		Æ ·95	to l., 𝔅.	„ „ [I. O. C. Pl. xix. 11.]

* Restruck on a coin of Hippostratus; for types see coin of Hippostratus, supra, p. 60, no. 15.

N

No.	Wt.	Metal. Size.	Obverse.	Reverse.
			ΒΑΣΙΛΕΩΣ ΒΑΣΙ-ΛΕΩΝ ΜΕΓΑΛΟΥ ΑΖΟΥ Elephant r.	ꛃꛃ∿ꛃꛃꛃ ꛃꛃ∿ ꛃꛃ? (*Maharajasa rajarajasa mahatasa Ayasa*). Humped bull r.
188		Æ 1·1	above, ·7 .	to r., ᛗ .
			ΒΑΣΙΛΕΩΣ ΜΕΓΑ-ΛΟΥ ΑΖΟΥ Ele-phant r.	ꛃꛃ? ꛃꛃ∿ ꛃꛃ∿ (*Maharajasa mahatasa Ayasa*). Humped bull r.
189		Æ ·45		[Pl. xix. 12.]
			ΒΑΣΙΛΕΩΣΒ]ΑΣΙΛΕΩΝΜΕΓΑΛΟΥΑΣ[Lion r.	ꛃꛃ? . . . . . ꛃꛃ∿ (*Maharaja . . . . . Ayasa*). Humped bull l.
190		Æ ·65	above, ꛃ .	above, ꛃ . [I. O. C.]

(o) *Billon; semi-barbarous coinage.*

No.	Wt.	Metal. Size.	Obverse.	Reverse.
			Corrupt legend. King r., on horseback; holds in r. hand ankus(?); before him, symbol ꛃ .*	ꛃꛃꛃꛃ ꛃꛃ∿ ꛃꛃ∿ ꛃꛃ? ꛃꛃꛃꛃꛃ (*Maharajasa mahatasa dhrami-kasà rajadirajasa Ayasa*). City l., turreted, and clad in chiton and peplum; r. hand advanced; in l., cornucopiae.
191	145·4	Ꞧ ·85		to l., Ꙃ ; to r., ☫ . [Pl. xx. 1.]
192	141·	Ꞧ ·8		,, ,, ,, ,,
193	142·2	Ꞧ ·8		,, ,, ,, ,,

* On most of these coins there is an appearance of various Indian letters in the obverse field which are not here inserted, it being doubtful whether they are not mere blunders.

No.	Wt.	Metal. Size.	Obverse.	Reverse.
			Corrupt legend. King r., on horseback ; holds in r. hand ankus (?); before him, symbol Ⴤ .	ᐯᏂᲧᏃ ᐯᎷᲚᜈᏌ ᐯᎩᲚᜈᏌ ᐯᎩᏏ ᐯᎩᲚᲧᏍᲚ (*Maharajasa mahatasa dhramikasa rajadirajasa Ayasa*). City l., turreted, and clad in chiton and peplum ; r. hand advanced ; in l., cornucopiae.
194	145·9	Æ ·85		to l., Ⴑ ; to r., 𝕏 .
195	131·5	Æ ·8		,, ,, ,, ,,
196	148·2	Æ ·85		,, ,, ,, 𝕏 . [I. O. C.]
197	144·	Æ ·75		,, ,, ,, ,, ,,
198	148·5	Æ ·85		,, ,, ,, ,, ,,
199	142·8	Æ ·8		,, ,, ,, ,, ,,

(π) *Billon; with name of Aspavarma.*

			BAΣIΛEΩΣ BAΣI-ΛEΩN MEΓAΛoY AZoY King r., on horseback ; holds ankus ; behind him, bow on saddle ; beneath, ☵ .	ᐯᎫᎡᏂᎡ ᐯᏃᎧ ᎫᎡᏃᏃᏃ ᐯᎩᏝᏝ ᐯᏝᏍᏃ (*Indravarma putrasa Aspavarmasa strategasa jayatasa*). Pallas r., armed ; her r. hand advanced ; in her l., spear and shield ; behind, star and ☵ .
200	157·3	Æ ·85	to r., Ⴥ .	to r., 𝕄; to l., uncertain letter. [Pl. xx. 2.]
201	140·3	Æ ·8	,, ,,	,, ,, ,, Ꮇ .
202	150·9	Æ ·8	,, ,,	,, ,, ,, Ꭲ .
203	156·9	Æ ·8	,, ,,	,, ,, ,, Ꮋ .
204	146·8	Æ ·8	,, ,,	,, ,, ,, ᐯ .
205	148·3	Æ ·8	,, ,,	,, ,, ,, ,,
206	130·5	Æ ·8	,, ,,	,, ,, ,, Ꮍ .

No.	Wt.	Metal. Size.	Obverse.	Reverse.
			ΒΑΣΙΛΕΩΣ ΒΑΣΙ-ΛΕΩΝ ΜΕΓΑΛΟΥ ΑΖΟΥ King r., on horseback; holds ankus; behind hìm, bow on saddle; beneath, �.	𐨤𐨗𐨪𐨟𐨪 𐨤𐨡𐨱 𐨟𐨩𐨿𐨤 𐨤𐨪𐨫𐨩 𐨤𐨡𐨭𐨦 (*Indravarma putrasa Aspavarma-sa strategasa jayatasa*). Pallas r., armed; her r. hand advanced; in her l., spear and shield; behind, star and ☿.
207	157·2	Æ ·85	to r., ♅ .	to r, 𐨬; to l., ς. [I. O. C.]
208	159·4	Æ 9	,, ,,	,, ,, ,, ,, ,,
209	150·	Æ ·85	,, ,,	,, ,, ,, ◡ . ,,
210	155·7	Æ ·8	,, ,,	,, ,, ,,
211	149·	Æ ·8	,, ,,	,, uncertain letter. ,,

AZES AND AZILISES.

(a) Silver.

			ΒΑΣΙΛΕΩΣ .. ΗΜ-ΓΑΛΟΥ ΑΖΛΙΣΟΥ The king r., on horseback; holds bow.	𐨤𐨱𐨪𐨗𐨭 𐨤 . . . . 𐨤𐨩𐨪𐨭 𐨤𐨫𐨩 (*Maharajasa [rajaraja]sa mahatasa Ayasa*). Zeus standing l., diad.; holds Nike and long sceptre.
1	31·7	Æ ·6	in front, ◡ .	to l., 𐨬𐨬; to r., 𐨙. [I. O. C. Pl. xx. 3.]

No.	Wt.	Metal. Size.	Obverse	Reverse.

AZILISES.

(a) *Silver; type, Zeus.*

No.	Wt.	Metal. Size.	Obverse	Reverse.
			ΒΑΣΙΛΕΩΣ ΒΑΣΙΛΕΩΝ ΜΕΓΑΛΟΥ ΑΖΙΛΙΣΟΥ The king r., on horseback; in r. hand, ankus; bow on saddle.	ᚱ᛬᛬ (*Maharajasa rajadirajasa mahatasa Ayilishasa*). Zeus r., diad., wearing himation; holds wreath (?) and long sceptre.
1	148·5	Æ 1·05	to r., ⊞.	to l., Λ ; to r., 7. [Pl. xx. 4.]

(β) *Silver; type, Dioscuri.*

			ΒΑΣΙΛΕΩΣ ΒΑΣΙΛΕΩΝ ΜΕΓΑΛΟΥ ΑΖΙΛΙΣΟΥ The king r., on horseback; holds ankus; bow on saddle.	ᚱ᛬᛬ (*Maharajasa rajadirajasa mahatasa Ayilishasa*). The Dioscuri, facing; each wears Phrygian cap and chlamys, and holds spear and sword.
2	146·2	Æ 1·05	to r., ⚭.	
3	150·4	Æ 1·05	„ ⚭ ; below, ⊔.	to l., ⊅ ; to r., ⚡. [Pl. xx. 5.]
4	33·3	Æ ·65	„ „	„ „ „ [I. O. C. Pl. xx. 6.]
			Similar.	Same inscr. One of the Dioscuri, facing, as above, but bearded and wearing chiton.
5	146·8	Æ 1·1	to r., ⚭.	to l., ⚡. [Pl. xx. 7.]
6	37·8	Æ ·6	to r., ⚭.	to l., ⚡. [Pl. xx. 8.]

No.	Wt.	Metal. Size.	Obverse.	Reverse.
				(γ) *Silver; type, City ?*
			ΒΑΣΙΛΕΩΣ ΒΑΣΙ-ΛΕΩΝ ΜΕΓΑΛΟΥ ΑΖΙΛΙΣΟΥ The king r., on horseback; holds lance couched.	ꔣꔳ∼∽ ꔳꔴꔵꔶꔷ ꔳꔴ∼∽ ꔳꔸꔹꔺꔻ (*Maharajasa rajarajasa mahatasa Ayilishasa*). City (?) l.; holds in r., uncertain object; in l., palm bound with fillet.
7	140·3	Æ 1·05		to l., ✠ Ƶ ; to r., ⅄. [Pl. xx. 9.]
8	149·8	Æ 1·05	to r., Ƶ.	„ „ „ „
9	146·2	Æ 1·	„ ⅄ Ƶ.	„ „ „ „ [I. O. C.]
10	139·5	Æ 1·	„ ꔳ „	„ „ „ „ „
11	144·9	Æ 1·1		„ Σ; „ ꔳ [Pl. xx. 10.]
12	148·5	Æ 1·05		„ ⊕ Ƭ; „ Ƶ.
13	35·8	Æ ·7		to l., ⊕ Ⴚ; to r., Ƶ.
14	35·3	Æ ·7		„ „ „ „
15	32·6	Æ ·65		„ ⊕; „ Ƶ. [Pl. xx. 11.]
16	32·9	Æ ·7		„ „ . „ Ƶ.
17	32·2	Æ 7		„ „ „ ꔸ.
18	34·7	Æ ·65		„ „ „ ꔳ.
19	36·	Æ ·7		„ „ „ Ƶ. [I. O. C.]
20	35·8	Æ ·65		„ ✠ ꔸ; „ ⅄.
21	35·	Æ ·65	to r., ꔳ.	„ „ „ „
22	36·9	Æ ·7	„ ꔼ Ƶ.	„ „

No.	Wt.	Metal. Size.	Obverse.	Reverse.
			(δ) Bronze; square; type, King on horseback.	
			ΒΑΣΙΛΕΩΣ ΒΑΣΙ-ΛΕΩΝ ΜΕΓΑΛΟΥ ΑΖΙΛΙΣΟΥ King r., on horseback; holds lance couched.	?T+IX? ?ꞁ∿U ?Yꞁ∿U (*Maharajasa mahatasa Ayilishasa*). Herakles, diad., naked, seated l.; holds in r. hand club, which rests on knee.
23	Æ ·9		to r., ⅄ Ƨ.	to l., ⅄ 🆘. [Pl. XXI. 1.]
24	Æ ·95		„ „	„ „ „
			Similar.	Same inscr. Elephant r.
25	Æ ·85			above, ⅄ 🆘.
26	Æ ·75			„ „ „ [I. O. C. Pl. XXI. 2.]
			Similar.	?ꞁ∿U ?Yꞁ⅄ꞁ ?Yꞁ∿U ?T+IX? (*Maharajasa rajarajasa mahatasa Ayilishasa*). Humped bull r.
27	Æ ·9			above, ⅄ Σ. [Pl. XXI. 3.]
28	Æ 1·05			„ Ⱥ ?.
29	Æ ·95			„ „ „ [I. O. C]
30	Æ 1·1			„ 🜨 Ψ.

No.	Wt.	Metal. Size.	Obverse.	Reverse.
			ΒΑΣΙΛΕΩΣ ΒΑΣΙ-ΛΕΩΝ ΜΕΓΑΛΟΥ ΑΖΙΛΙΣΟΥ King r., on horseback ; holds lance couched.	ꡒ⁓ ꡒꡒꡒ ꡒ⁓ ꡒꡒꡒ (*Maharajasa rajarajasa mahatasa Ayilishasa*). Humped bull l.
31		Æ1·05		above, Ψ ᛘ. (restruck coin).
32		Æ ·95	to r., ꡒ.	„ Σ ꡒ.
33		Æ ·9	(king to l.)	„ „ „
			(ε) *Bronze ; square ; type, King (?) standing.*	
			ΒΑΣΙΛΕΩΣ ΒΑΣΙ-ΛΕΩΝ ΜΕΓΑΛΟΥ ΑΖΙΛΙΣΟΥ The king(?) standing r., clad in helmet and cloak ; holds in l. hand, shield ; r. advanced.	ꡒ⁓ ꡒꡒꡒꡒ ꡒꡒꡒ ꡒꡒꡒ (*Maharajasa rajadirajasa mahatasa Ayilishasa*). Nike (?) r., unwinged, clad in short chiton, with inflated veil over her head ; holds in r. hand wreath.
34		Æ ·9	to r., ᛘ.	to r., ꡒ. [Pl. xxi. 4.]
35		Æ 1·		
36		Æ ·85	„ „	to l., Ψ ; to r., uncertain letter. [I. O. C.]
37		Æ ·95	„ „	„ „ „ „ „
			(ζ) *Bronze ; square ; other types.*	
			ΒΑΣΙΛΕΩΣ [ΒΑΣΙ-ΛΕΩΝ ΜΕΓΑ]ΛΥ ΑΖΙΛΙΣΥ Herakles, facing, crowning himself ; holds in l. hand club and lion's skin.	ꡒ⁓ ꡒꡒꡒꡒ ꡒꡒꡒ ꡒꡒꡒ (*Maharajasa rajadirajasa mahatasa Ayilishasa*). Horse standing r.
38		Æ ·9	to l., ꡒ.	above, ꡒ.
39		Æ ·95	„ „	in field, Ψ ꡒ. [I. O C. Pl. xxi. 5.]

No.	Wt.	Metal. Size.	Obverse.	Reverse.
			ΒΑΣΙΛΕΩΣ ΒΑΣΙ-ΛΕΩΝ ΜΕΓΑΛ•Υ ΑΖΙΛΙΣ•Υ Male figure, facing, clad in himation, head turned to r.; holds in r. hand, sceptre; in l., uncertain object.	𐨤𐨪~𐨂 𐨤𐨩𐨪𐨮𐨩𐨩 𐨤𐨩𐨪~𐨂 𐨤𐨟𐨱𐨐 𐨩 (*Maharajasa rajadirajasa mahatasa Ayilishasa*). Lion r., looking back.
40		Æ 1·05	to l., 𝕏.	above, 𐨤. [I. O. C. Pl. xxi. 6.]
			Inscr. obscure. Elephant l.	Inscr. obscure; ends 𐨤𐨟𐨱𐨐 𐨩 (*Ayilishasa*). Humped bull l.
41		Æ 1·05		to l., mon. [I. O. C.]

o

No.	Wt.	Metal. Size.	Obverse.	Reverse.
			SPALAHORES, WITH VONONES.	
			(α) *Silver.*	
			ΒΑΣΙΛΕΩΣ ΒΑΣΙ-ΛΕΩΝ ΜΕΓΑΛΟΥ ΟΝΩΝΟΥ King r., on horseback; holds lance couched.	𐨤𐨲𐨨𐨪 𐨲𐨿𐨪 𐨩𐨿𐨪.∿𐨩 𐨤𐨿𐨪𐨤𐨪 (*Māhāraja bhrata dhramikasa Spalahorasa*). Zeus, laur., facing, clad in himation; holds thunderbolt and long sceptre.
1	144·5	Æ1·05		to r., ℞. [I. O. C. Pl. xxi. 7.]
2	37·5	Æ ·6		to r., ℞.
3	37·3	Æ ·7		„ „ [Pl. xxi. 8.]
4	38·	Æ ·65		to l., ⊞.
5	37·8	Æ ·6		„ „
			(β) *Bronze; square.*	
			ΒΑΣΙΛΕΩΣ ΒΑΣΙ-ΛΕΩΝ ΜΕΓΑΛΟΥ ΟΝΩΝΟΥ Herakles, facing; holds in l. hand, club and lion's skin; and with r., crowns himself.	𐨤𐨲𐨨𐨪 𐨲𐨿𐨪 𐨩𐨿𐨪.∿𐨩 𐨤𐨿𐨪𐨤𐨪 (*Māhāraja bhrata dhramikasa Spalahorasa*). Pallas l., wearing helmet; holds in r. hand, wreath; in l., spear and shield bound with fillet; sword slung round waist.
6		Æ ·85		to l., ⊞.
7		Æ ·8		„ „ [Pl. xxi. 9.]

No.	Wt.	Metal. Size.	Obverse.	Reverse.
			SPALAGADAMES, WITH VONONES.	
			(α) *Silver.*	
			ΒΑΣΙΛΕΩΣ ΒΑΣΙΛΕΩΝ ΜΕΓΑΛΟΥ ΟΝΩΝΟΥ King r., on horseback; holds lance couched.	𐨯𐨿𐨤𐨫𐨱𐨆𐨪 𐨤𐨂𐨟𐨿𐨪𐨯 𐨢𐨿𐨪𐨨𐨁𐨀𐨯 𐨯𐨿𐨤𐨫𐨒𐨡𐨨𐨯 *Spalahora putrāsa dhramiasa Spalagadamasa*). Zeus, facing, laur., clad in himation; holds thunderbolt and long sceptre.
1	36·1	AR ·65		to l., [monogram].
2	36·5	AR ·7		" " [Pl. xxi. 10.]
3	36·8	AR ·6		" [monogram].
4	36·2	AR ·65		" " [I. O. C.]
			(β) *Bronze; square.*	
			ΒΑΣΙΛΕΩΣ ΒΑΣΙΛΕΩΝ ΜΕΓΑΛΟΥ ΟΝΩΝΟΥ Herakles, facing; holds in l. hand, club and lion's skin; and with r., crowns himself.	𐨯𐨿𐨤𐨫𐨱𐨆𐨪 𐨤𐨂𐨟𐨿𐨪𐨯 𐨢𐨿𐨪𐨨𐨁𐨀𐨯 𐨯𐨿𐨤𐨫𐨒𐨡𐨨𐨯 *Spalahora putrāsa dhramiasa Spalagada masa*). Pallas l., wearing helmet; holds in r. hand, wreath (?); in l., spear and shield bound with fillet; sword slung round waist.
5		Æ ·75		to l., [monogram].
6		Æ ·8		" " [Pl. xxi. 11.]

No.	Wt.	Metal. Size.	Obverse.	Reverse.
			SPALAGADAMES, WITH SPALYRIS.	
			(a) *Bronze; square.*	
			ϹΠΑΛΥΡΙΟϹ ΔΙΚΑΙ- ΟΥ ΑΔΕΛΦΟΥ ΤΟΥ ΒΑϹΙΛΕΩϹ King r., on horseback.	𐨤𐨪𐨱𐨨 𐨤·𐨧𐨪 𐨪𐨫𐨡𐨿 𐨤𐨂𐨟𐨿𐨪𐨿 *Spalahora putrāsa dhramiasa Spalagadamasa).* Herakles, diad., seated l. on rocks; holds in r. hand, club, which rests on knee.
1		Æ ·85		to l., ⊛. [Pl. xxi. 12.]
2		Æ ·8		„ „
3		Æ ·85		„ ⊠.
			SPALIRISES; AS KING'S BROTHER.	
			(a) *Silver.*	
			ΒΑϹΙΛΕΩϹ ΑΔΕΛ- ΦΟΥ ϹΠΑΛΙΡΙϹΟΥ King r., on horseback; holds lance couched.	𐨤𐨪𐨱𐨨 ·𐨧𐨿𐨪* 𐨪𐨫 𐨤𐨧𐨪𐨿 *(Māhāraja bhrahā dhramiasa Spalirisasa).* Zeus, facing, wearing himation; holds thunderbolt and long sceptre.
1	36·6	Æ ·55		to l., ⊠. [Pl. xxii. 1.]
2	26·7	Æ ·6		„ „

* Or ·𐨧𐨿𐨪 *bhratrā.* V. Sallet writes (p. 352), die Form *bhraha* für Bruder wird von sachkundiger Seite für berechtigt erklärt.

No.	Wt.	Metal. Size.	Obverse.	Reverse.

SPALIRISES ; AS KING.

(a) *Bronze; square.*

BACIΛEWN BACIΛ-EWC MEΓAΛOY CΠAΛIPICOY King, standing l. ; holds battle-axe ; bow at his side.

𐨤𐨱𐨪.~𐨜 𐨤𐨩𐨪~ 𐨤 𐨧𐨩𐨱𐨱𐨪 (*Maharajasa māhātakasa Spalirisasa*). Zeus, radiate, seated l. on throne ; r. hand extended ; in l., sceptre.

No.	Wt.	Metal. Size.	Obverse.	Reverse.
1		Æ ·9		to r., ⊕ .
2		Æ ·9		,, ,, *
3		Æ ·95		
4		Æ ·9		,, ,, [I. O. C. Pl. XXII. 2.]
5		Æ ·9		,, ⊗ . [I. O. C.]

* Restruck on copper of Vonones with Spalahores or Spalagadames (?). Club of Herakles seen on obv. (?).

No.	Wt.	Metal. Size.	Obverse.	Reverse.

SPALIRISES, WITH AZES.

(a) Silver.

			BACIΛEWC MEΓA-ΛOY PΠAΛIPICOY King r., on horseback; holds lance couched.	ꡭꡭꡭ.ꡭꡭ ꡭꡭꡭꡭ ꡭꡭꡭ (*Maharajasa mahātakasa Ayasa*). Zeus, facing, laur., clad in himation; holds thunderbolt and long sceptre.
1	37·7	Æ ·6		to l., ⊞; to r., ꡭ.
2	37·8	Æ ·6		,, ,, ,, ,,
3	34·5	Æ ·65		,, ,, ,, [I. O. C. Pl. xxii. 3.]
4	30·9	Æ ·65		,, ,, ,, ,, [I. O. C.]

(β) Bronze; round.

			BACIΛEWC MEΓA-ΛOY IΠAΛIPICOY King r., on horseback; holds ankus.	ꡭꡭꡭ.ꡭꡭ ꡭꡭꡭꡭ ꡭꡭꡭ (*Maharajasa mahātakasa Ayasa*). Strung bow and arrow l.
5		Æ ·95		above, ⊗. [Pl. xxii. 4.]

No.	Wt.	Metal. Size.	Obverse.	Reverse.

GONDOPHARES.

(a) Base silver ; type, Zeus.

			BACIΛEШICIΛEШN MEΓAΛI VИΔOΦPP The king r., on horseback ; arm extended ; in front, ☿ .	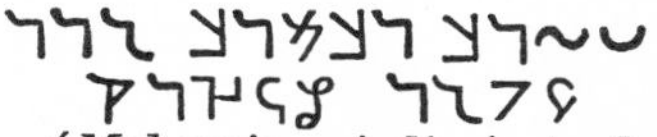 � (Maharaja rajadiraja tradata devatrata* Gudapharasa). Zeus, naked to waist, standing r. ; r. arm extended ; in l., long sceptre.
1	144·2	Æ ·9		to l., ⊕; to r., 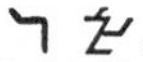 ꓶ ꙮ . [I. O. C. Pl. xxii. 5.]
2	136·5	Æ ·95	inscr. **BACIΛEШC BACIΛEШN** &c.	„ „ B; „ ꙮ ꓳ. [I. O. C.]

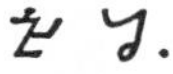

(β) Base silver ; type, Pallas.

			BACIΛE . BACIΛEШN MEΓAΛ· ꓩNΔOΦEPPO The king, diad., r., on horseback ; to r., ☿ .	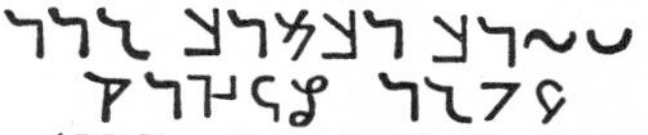 (Maharaja rajadiraja tradata devatrata Gudapharasa). Pallas r., armed ; in her l. hand, spear and shield ; her r. advanced.
3	142·	Æ ·95		to l., ꙮ; to r.,  ∪ ⊕ . [Pl. xxii. 6.]
4	143·	Æ ·9	inscr. **BACIΛEШC □V □E□V VИΔ□ □EPP**	„ „ „ „ „
			Inscr. barbarous. Head of the king r., diad.	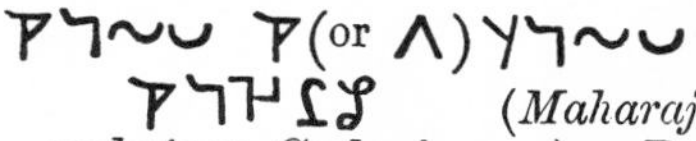 ꓔꓶ∪∪ ꓒ(or Λ)ꓬꓶ∪∪ (Maharajasa mahatasa Gudapharasa). Pallas r., fighting ; holds thunderbolt and shield.
5	37·6	Æ ·45		in field, 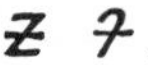 ꓜ � . [Pl. xxii. 7.]
6	38·5	Æ ·45		„ „ „
7	40·6	Æ ·5		„ „ „

* *Devatrāta*, protected by the Gods. This word has been read by Gen. Cunningham *Devahada*, as a rendering of θεότροπος.

No.	Wt.	Metal. Size.	Obverse.	Reverse.
			(γ) *Base silver; type, Siva.*	
			BACIΛEωC BACI-ΛEωN MEΓAΛOY VNΔOΦEPPOY The king l., on horseback; r. hand raised; behind him, Nike flying l., holding wreath and palm; to l., ☿ .	(Kharoshthi inscription) (*Maharajasa rajarajasa tradatasa devatratasa Gudapharasa*). Siva, facing; holds in r. hand, trident; in l., palm.
8	146·2	Æ ·95		to l., 6; to r., ᛦ . [Pl. XXII. 8.] ☸
9	137·4	Æ ·95	below, ⅞ .	„ „ (Λ for Ӡ in inscr.) „ „ [I. O. C.]
			BACIΛEωN BACI-ΛEωN ΓOИΔOΦA-ΓOY The king r., on horseback; holds ankus in extended r. hand; to r., ☿ .	(Kharoshthi inscription) (*Maharaja rajaraja mahatasa . . devatrata Gudapharasa*). Siva, facing; r. extended; in l., trident.
10	145·8	Æ ·95	below, ⵣ .	to l., ⊞; to r., mon. [I. O. C. Pl. XXII. 9.]
11	146·7	Æ ·9	„ „	„ „ „ „
			(δ) *Base silver; type, Nike.*	
			BA CIΛE The king, diad., seated l. on throne with back; on the top of which ☿ ☿ ; r. hand raised.	ΛOVVNΔOΦ Nike r.; holds wreath and palm.
† 12	108·5	Æ ·85		to l., Ύ; to r., Φ . [Pl. XXII. 10.]

* The missing letters look like (Kharoshthi) *mita* (for *mitra?*).

† This coin, as well as some of those which precede it, is apparently wholly or almost wholly made of copper; but the nature of the types indicates that it was intended to pass among the debased silver coins of the period.

No.	Wt.	Metal. Size.	Obverse.	Reverse.
			(ϵ) *Copper ; type, Nike.*	
			BACIΛEΩC CΩTH-POC YNΔoΦEP-POV Bust of the king r., diad.	ᛏᛁᛝᛚ ᛏᚠᛏᚼᚲᛎ ᛏᛃᛁᛚ (*Maharajasa Gudaphanasa tradatasa*). Nike r. ; holds wreath and palm.
13		Æ ·9		
14		Æ 1·		
15		Æ ·95		
16		Æ ·95		
17		Æ ·85	(ω for Ω in inscr.).	
18		Æ ·95		
19		Æ ·9		
20		Æ ·9		
21		Æ ·9	(inscr. begins BACIΛ-EoN).	[I. O. C. Pl. xxii. 11.]
			(ζ) *Bronze ; square.*	
			ΦAΓoV EΓAΛoV ΓoNΔA *sic.* King l., on horseback ; received by Nike, who holds wreath.	ᛏᛚᛉᛞᚼᛁ ᛏᚼᛃᛃ . . . . . ᛏᛁᚼᚲᛎ ᛏᛁᛚᛦᛎ (. . . . . *dhamikasa apratihatasa devatratasa* (*devahadasa*) *Gadapharasa*). ᛎ .
22		Æ ·85		to l., ᛃ ; to r., ᛏ . [I. O. C. Pl. xxii. 12.]

P

No.	Wt.	Metal. Size.	Obverse.	Reverse.
			(η) Base silver ; with inscr. Sasasa.	
			Inscr. corrupt. The king, diad., r., on horseback ; r. hand raised ; to r., ☿ .	𐨤𐨪𐨫𐨢𐨀 𐨤𐨪𐨯𐨆 𐨤𐨩𐨪𐨯𐨆 𐨤𐨪𐨱𐨌𐨆 (*Maharajasa mahatasa devatratasa (devaha-dasa) Gadapharasa)* ; in ex., 𐨤𐨤𐨤 (*Sasasa*). Zeus, diad., standing r. ; r. hand advanced ; in l., long sceptre ; to l., ☒ .
23	149·8	Æ ·9	below, *h*; to r., ⅄ .	to l., uncertain letter; to r., ⅀ 𐀀𐀀 *h*.
24	153·4	Æ ·85	„ 𐀀 *h*.	below, **A**; to r., 𐀀 *h*.
25	138·	Æ ·8	„ uncertain letters.	„ **B**; „ „ „
26	148·	Æ ·8	„ 𐀀 *h*.	„ **N**; „ „ „
27	129·5	Æ ·8	„ „ „	„ „ „ „ „
28	154·3	Æ ·85	„ ⅄ „	„ 𐀀𐀀; „ „ „
29	134·9	Æ ·8	(obscure).	(obscure).
			Similar.	.... 𐨤𐨩𐨪𐨌𐨩𐨪 𐨤𐨩𐨪𐨯𐨆 𐨤𐨪𐨱𐨌𐨆 (*Maharajasa rajadirajasa........ Gadapharasa)*; in ex., 𐨤𐨤𐨤 (*Sasasa*). Zeus l.; Nike in extended r. hand.
30	152·5	Æ ·8	to r., 𐀀 .	to l., ⊞; to r., ℞ 𐀀 .
				[I. O. C. Pl. xxii. 13.]
31	151·8	Æ ·85	„ „	„ „ „ „ [I. O. C.]
32	150·7	Æ ·8	„ ꓵ.	„ „ „ „ „

No.	Wt.	Metal. Size.	Obverse.	Reverse.

ABDAGASES.

(a) *Copper; as King.*

			BACIΛEⲰC CⲰTH-POC A[BΔAΓ]ACOV Bust of the king r., diad.	𐨤 𐨣𐨱𐨪𐨗𐨯 𐨤𐨯𐨱𐨟𐨮𐨯 𐨤𐨪𐨣𐨮 (*Tradatasa maharajasa Avadaga-sasa*). Nike r., holding wreath and palm.
1		Æ ·85		[Pl. xxiii. 1.]
2		Æ ·85		to l., uncertain letters.
3		Æ ·9		
4		Æ ·9	(inscr. **BACIΛEYC CⲰTHP . . . .**).	

(β) *Base silver; as King's nephew.*

			BAΞIΛEYоNTоΞ BAΞIΛEⲰNI AB-ΔAΓAΞоY (The **BA** of Abdagases' name read sometimes as the first letters of **BAΞIΛ-EYоNTоΞ**; the letter which follows **BA-ΞIΛEⲰN** is uncertain [**I** or **Ξ**?]). The king l., on horseback; in front, 𐨮 .	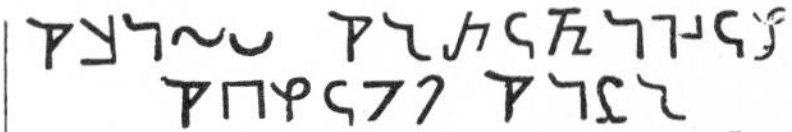 𐨤𐨯𐨱𐨟𐨮𐨯 𐨤𐨫𐨱𐨮𐨟𐨪𐨤𐨯 𐨤𐨣𐨱𐨪𐨗𐨯 𐨤𐨪𐨣𐨮 (*Gadapharabhradaputrasa maharajasa tradatasa Avadagasasa*). Zeus, standing r. ; holds sceptre ; r. hand advanced.
5	150·	Æ ·85	to l., �7.	 to l., 𐨮 𐨣 ; to r., 𐨤 𐨫 .
6	155·5	Æ ·9	,, ,,	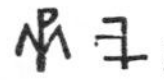 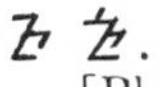 ,, 𐨨 𐨃 ; ,, 𐨤 𐨬 . [Pl. xxiii. 2]
7	150 1	Æ ·85	,, ,,	,, ,, ,, ,, ,, ,,

No.	Wt.	Metal. Size.	Obverse.	Reverse.
			ΒΑΣΙΛΕΥοΝΤοΣ ΒΑΣΙΛΕΩΝΙ ΑΒ-ΔΑΓΑΣοΥ (The ΒΑ of Abdagases' name read sometimes as the first letters of ΒΑΣΙΛ-ΕΥοΝΤοΣ; the letter which follows ΒΑ-ΣΙΛΕΩΝ is uncertain [Ι or Σ?]). The king l., on horseback; in front, ⚹.	(*Gadapharabhradaputrasa maharajasa tradatasa Avadagasasa*). Zeus, standing r. ; holds sceptre ; r. hand advanced.
8	149·5	Æ ·85		to l., 𐰩 𐰴 ; to r., 𐰔 𐰵 . [I. O. C.]
9	149·2	Æ ·85	to l., 𐰴 .	,, ,, ,, **B** ; ,, ,, ,,
10	146·4	Æ ·8	,, 𐰢 .	,, 𐰼 ,, ,, ,, ,,
11	142·5	Æ ·9	,, 𐰧 .	,, ,, ,, ,, ,, ,,
12	158·5	Æ ·85	,, 𐰽 .	,, ,, ,, ,, ,, ,,
13	142·4	Æ ·95	type r.	,, ,, ,, 𐰔 𐰵 .
14	150·2	Æ ·95	,,	,, ,, ,, ,, 𐰽 . [I. O. C.]
15	124·4	Æ ·85	,,	,, ,, ,, ,, 𐰔 𐰵 .
16	121·5	Æ ·85	inscr. ΓΥ]ΝΔΙΦΕΡΟΑ-ΔΕΛΦΙ[ΔΕΩΣ	,, 𐰼 ; ,, 𐰩 𐰧 . [Pl. xxiii. 3.]

No.	Wt.	Metal. Size.	Obverse.	Reverse.
				ORTHAGNES.
				(a) *Bronze.*
			BACIΛЄVC BACI-ΛЄWN MЄΓAC OPΘAΓNHC Bust of the king l, diad.; wears torquis.	₹ΥꓶꓬΥꓶ ₹Υꓶ∿ꓴ ·ꓶꓒ₹ ꓶꓵꓚꓒ ₹Υꓶ∿ꓴ (*Maharajasa rajadirajasa maha-tasa Gudaphara sagaba.?*).* Nike r.; holds wreath and palm.
1	Æ ·9			to l., ꓶꓥ; to r., ꓒ. [Pl. XXIII. 9.]
2	Æ 1·05			„ „ „ „ ꓕ.
3	Æ ·95			„ ₹ ⱷ; „ „
4	Æ ·9			„ Υ; „ „ (last letter of inscr. absent).
5	Æ ·9			„ „ „ „ „ „
6	Æ 1·05		inscr. ends OPΘAΓN.	to l., uncertain letter; to r., ꓕ.
7	Æ ·95		B MЄΓAΛOY OPΘAΓNOY Similar.	Illegible inscr. Similar type. to l., ꟼ; to r., ꓴ.

* This is Gen. Cunningham's reading: *sagaba* he supposes to stand for *sagarbha*, 'brother.' On no. 2 of the British Museum coins there is another letter at the end, which looks like ꓚ (*na* or *da*), but which may be a badly formed ₹.

No.	Wt.	Metal. Size.	Obverse.	Reverse.

PACORES.

(a) Bronze.

			BACIΛEYC BACI-ΛEWN MEΓAC ΠΑΚΟΡΗC Bust of the king l., wears torquis; behind, star.	ᛘᚦᚱᚼᛉᚱ ᛘᚦᛉᚾᚢ ᛘᚦᚼᚼ ᛘᚦᚾᚢ (Maharajasa rajadirajasa mahatasa Pakurasa). Nike l.; holding wreath and palm.
1	Æ ·95			to l., uncertain letter; to r., ᚼᚱ. [Pl. XXIII. 8.]
2	Æ ·85			„ ᚴ; „ „
3	Æ 1·			„ uncertain letter; „ „
4	Æ 1·			„ ᛏ; „ „
5	Æ 1·			„ „ „ „
6	Æ ·9			„ uncertain letter; „ „

ZEIONISES.

(a) Silver; type, King on horseback.

			CATPAΓY The king ZE..NƆOY r., on horseback; in r. hand whip; bow tied to saddle; to r., ⚕.	ᛘᚾᚼ ᛘᚼᛈᛉ ᛘᛇᛂ[ᛘᛉᚠᛂᛉ ᛘᚼᛈᛉ ([Mani?]gulasa chhatrapasa putrasa chhatrapasa Jihuniasa). King r., facing a City who wears mural crown, and holds wreath and cornucopiae.
1	157·6	Æ 1·05	beneath, ᛉ ᚼ.	to l, ᛐ; to r., ᚼᚱ. [Pl. XXIII. 4.]
2	139·4	Æ 1·05	„ ᛉ and other letters.	„ „ „ „ [I. O. C.]

No.	Wt.	Metal. Size.	Obverse.	Reverse.
			(β) *Bronze; types, lion and bull.*	
			]ΛΟΥΥΙΥϹΑΤΡΑΠ[Humped bull r.; above, 𝕪̈.	⟨Mani?⟩* *gulaputrasa chhatrapasa* *Jihuniasa*). Lion r.
3		Æ 1·	to r., 𐨤.	to l., 𐨋; to r., 𐨩; below, 2. [Pl. xxiii. 5.]
4		Æ 1·	„ 𐨗.	„ „ „ 3.
			UNCERTAIN KINGS.	
			(α) *Bronze; square.*	
			Illegible Greek inscription; in which sometimes the word ϹΑΤ-ΠΑΠ and sometimes ΧΑΡΑΝШ is visible. King r., on horseback; lance couched.	Illegible Indian inscription; the words 𐨯𐨟𐨿𐨪𐨤𐨯 (*chhatrapasa*) and 𐨤𐨂𐨟𐨿𐨪𐨯 (*putrasa*) sometimes visible. Lion r.
1		Æ 1·	to r., 𐨧.	above, 𐨱; to r., 𐨋.
2		Æ 1·	„ „	„ „ „ „
3		Æ 1·	„ „	„ „ „ „ [Pl. xxiii. 6.]
4		Æ ·85	„ „	„ „ „ „ [I. O. C.]
5		Æ ·8	„ 𐨤.	„ „ „ „ „
6		Æ ·8	„ 𐨤.	„ 𐨣 „ „ „

* Or *mañigulasa.* This is supposed to give us the name of the father of Zeionises. The word *Jihuniasa* is not clear on any British Museum specimens in bronze.

No.	Wt.	Metal. Size.	Obverse.	Reverse.
			(β) *Bronze; round.*	
			Debased Greek legend. Humped bull r.; above, ♨.	Undetermined Indian legend. Bactrian camel r.
7		Æ ·9	to r., uncertain letter.	to r., ฿; above, ƕ.
8		Æ ·85	„ „	„ „
9		Æ ·9	„ „	„ uncertain letter.
10		Æ ·95	„ ♫.	„ Υ. [Pl. xxiii. 7.]
11		Æ ·9	„ ⅃.	„ ♄.
12		Æ ·95	„ „	„ uncertain letter. (inscr. ꓶꓥꓹꓩꓥꓽ ꓶꓥꓼ∿∪ &c.)
13		Æ ·9		to r., uncertain letter.
14		Æ ·9	„ ♫.	above, uncertain letter; to r., Ƨ Υ.
15		Æ ·75	above, **BA** ♨; to r., uncertain letter.	to r., uncertain letter. (inscr. ꓷΥꓼ∿∪ &c.)
16		Æ ·65	„ „	to r., uncertain letter.

[Various readings of these two classes of coins have been published by Gen. Cunningham, *J. A. S. B.* 1854, pp. 695, 698; and by von Sallet, *Zeitsch. f. Num.* 1879, 369, 370. The British Museum specimens are not sufficiently well-preserved to enable us to give any certain readings].

No.	Wt.	Metal. Size.	Obverse.	Reverse.
			SANABARES.	
			(a) Silver.	
1	58·5	Æ ·75	Bust of the king l., wearing tiara of late Parthian form, and torquis; behind, ᴫ ⊓ (*ath*).	BACIΛEYC MEΓAC CANABA King dressed in Parthian style, seated r. on throne with back; holds bow. in front, Ǣ; above, ΓIT. [Pl. xxiii. 10.]
			(β) Bronze; Parthian class.	
2		Æ ·65	Head of the king l., diad. Inscr. (?)	BACIΛE CANABAPHC King seated r. on stool; holds bow. in front, ⊓. [Pl. xxiii. 11.]
3		Æ ·65		„ „
4		Æ ·6		„ ⋀⊓. (barbarous).
			(γ) Bronze; Bactrian class.	
5		Æ ·85	BAΣIΛEYΣ ... ? (corrupt). Bust of the king l., wearing tiara.	.... CANAᴄAPOY Nike r., holds wreath. [Pl. xxiii. 12.]

Q

No.	Wt.	Metal. Size.	Obverse.	Reverse.
			### BASILEUS SOTER MEGAS. *(a) Base silver; with Greek and Indian legends.*	
			BACIΛEYC BA]CI-ΛEYωN CωTHP MEΓAC The king r., on horseback; r. hand advanced; to r., ⳨ .	𐨤𐨩𐨪[𐨩𐨪 𐨤𐨩𐨪~𐨜 𐨤𐨪𐨱𐨕 𐨤𐨪~[𐨜 (*Maharajasa raja]dirajasa [ma]-hatasa tradatasa*). Zeus, standing r., clad in himation; r. hand raised; in l., sceptre.
1	146·4	Æ ·9		to l, � ; to r., uncertain object. [Pl. xxiv. 1.]
			(β) Copper; with Greek legends.	
			Bust of the king r., diad. and radiate; hand holds lance, bound with fillet; behind, ⳨ .	**BACIΛEVC BACIΛEVωN CωTHP MEΓAC** (frequently blundered). The king r., on horse-back, diad.; holds ankus? to r., ⳨ .
2		Æ ·8		
3		Æ ·8		[Pl. xxiv. 2.]
4		Æ ·8		
5		Æ ·8		[I. O. C.　Pl. xxiv. 3.]
6		Æ ·8		[I. O. C.]
7		Æ ·8		
8		Æ ·9		
9		Æ ·8		

No.	Wt.	Metal. Size.	Obverse.	Reverse.
10		Æ ·85	Bust of the king r., diad. and radiate ; hand holds lance, bound with fillet ; behind, 👤.	BACIΛEVC BACIΛEVωN CωTHP MEΓAC (frequently blundered). The king r., on horse-back, diad. ; holds ankus? to r., 👤.
11		Æ ·75		(inscr. ends BACIΛEωNCωTH).
12		Æ ·8		(inscr. barbarous). [I. O. C.]
13		Æ ·55	Similar.	BACIΛEVC BACIΛEVωN CωTHP M Similar.
14		Æ ·55		
15		Æ ·6		
16		Æ ·5		
17		Æ ·5		
18		Æ ·55		
19		Æ ·6		[I. O. C. Pl. xxiv. 4.]
20		Æ ·5		
21		Æ ·5		[I. O. C.]
22		Æ ·55		(inscr. barbarous).

No.	Wt.	Metal. Size.	Obverse.	Reverse.
			Bust of the king r., diad.; to r., ⚏.	]BACIΛ[ЄωN]CωTHPM[Zeus, standing l.; holds in r. hand, thunderbolt over altar; in l., sceptre.
23		Æ ·7		
24		Æ ·7		
25		Æ ·7		(inscr. . . BACIΛEYωN . . . . .). [Pl. xxiv. 5.]
			Bust of the king l., wearing crested helmet; in r. hand, lance: fillet border.	BACIΛEV BACIΛEVω[N C]ωTHP MЄΓAC King on horseback r., holding ankus; to r., ⚏.
26		Æ ·95	to l., �•; to r., ⚏.	
27		Æ ·95	,, ,, ,, ,,	[I. O. C. Pl. xxiv. 6.]

HERAÜS (ERAÜS).

(a) Silver.

			Bust of the king r., diad.: fillet-border.	TY/ANNOYNTOC H/AOY ΣAN A NO//ANOY* The king r., on horseback; bow and quiver tied to saddle; behind, Nike r., crowning him.
1	184·4	Æ 1·2		in field r., B . [Pl. xxiv. 7.]

* As to this legend, see Introduction.

HYRCODES.

(a) *Silver; type, a Deity standing.*

No.	Wt.	Metal. Size.	Obverse.	Reverse.
			ΥΡΚѠΔΟΥ Bust of the king with peaked beard r., diad.	**ΜΑΚΑΡΟΥ ΑΡΔΗΘΡΟΥ** Figure of a Deity (?), facing; holds spear in r. hand; flames on shoulders.
1	44·9	Æ ·65		[Pl. xxiv. 8.]
2	43·5	Æ ·7		
3	45·2	Æ ·65		[I. O. C.]
4	27·5	Æ ·7		
			ΥLΚѠΔΟΥ Similar.	**ΟΔΚΑΡΟ ΟѴΗΟΡ** Similar.
5	44·	Æ ·7		
6	42·5	Æ ·65		[I. O. C.]
7	39·7	Æ ·65		[Pl. xxiv. 9.]
8	51·5	Æ ·7		
			Barbarous imitation of the above.	Barbarous imitation.
9	30·	Æ ·55		[I. O. C.]
10	20·2	Æ ·55		
11	23·2	Æ ·6		
12	26·	Æ ·6		[Pl. xxiv. 10.]
13	17·5	Æ ·55		

No.	Wt.	Metal. Size.	Obverse.	Reverse.
			Barbarous imitation further degraded.	Barbarous imitation.
14	34·4	Æ ·55		[I. O. C.]
15	19·	Æ ·5		
16	17·6	Æ ·55		
17	12·3	Æ ·5		
18	10·	Æ ·55		
19	13·8	Æ ·45		
20	10·1	Æ ·4		[Pl. xxiv. 11.]
			(β) *Silver; type, horse.*	
			VPKωΔ Bust of the king r., diad.	VPKωΔ Forepart of bridled horse r.
21	23·3	Æ ·55		
22	23·8	Æ ·5		[Pl. xxiv. 12.]
23	22·5	Æ ·5		
24	14·	Æ ·45		[I. O. C.]
25	10·8	Æ ·5		
26	14·2	Æ ·45		
27	14·	Æ ·5	(barbarous legend).	(barbarous legend). [Pl. xxiv. 13.]
28	11·6	Æ ·5	,,	,,

No.	Wt.	Metal. Size.	Obverse.	Reverse.
			KINGS OF UNCERTAIN NAME.	
			SAPADBIZES (?).	
			(a) *Silver.*	
			Bust of a king r., in helmet like that of Eucratides.	NANAIA Lion r. NANAIA
1	25·3	Æ ·65	behind, ΑΓΕΕΙ ΗΛ	above, Λ̆.
2	26·2	Æ ·6	„ ΣΑΠΑΔΒΙΖ	„ „ [I. O. C. Pl. xxiv. 14.]
3	31·5	Æ ·6	„ ΣΑΠΑΔ?ΒΙΖΗΣ	„ „ [I. O. C. Pl. xxiv. 15.]
			PHSEIGACHARIS (?).	
			(a) *Silver.*	
			Bust of Scythian king r., diad.	ΦΣΕΙΓΑ Herakles, facing; holds ΧΑΓΙΣ in r. hand, club; in l., lion's skin.
1	37 6	Æ ·6		[I. O. C. Pl. xxiv. 16.]
2	36·8	Æ ·6		

No.	Wt.	Metal. Size.	Obverse.	Reverse.
			HERMAEUS AND KADPHISES I. (a) Copper ; type of rev., Herakles.	
			ΒΑΣΙΛΕΩΣ ΣΤΗ-ΡΟΣ ΣΥ ΕΡΜΑΙΟΥ (often corrupted). Bust of Hermaeus r., diad.	ΤΨϽΛ ϚՐⰅ ΤΤⰅⰃУⰅ* ՐϚ╫ՍⰔ (Kujula kasasa kushana yavu(?)gasa dhramaṭhi-dasa). Herakles, facing, diad.; holds in r. hand, club; in l., lion's skin.
1		Æ ·9		
2		Æ ·85		
3		Æ ·9		
4		Æ ·9		[I. O. C. Pl. xxv. 1.]
5		Æ ·9		
6		Æ ·9		[I. O. C.]
7		Æ ·9		
8		Æ ·9		
9		Æ ·85		
10		Æ ·85		

* This reading is made up from several specimens. General Cunning-ham transliterates the last two words *yathagasa dharmapidasa* (*J. A. S. B.*, 1854). The reading of the last word adopted in the text is Lassen's.

No.	Wt.	Metal. Size.	Obverse.	Reverse.
			ΒΑΣΙΛΕΩΣ ΣΤΗ-ΡΟΣ ΣΥ ΕΡΜΑΙΟΥ (often corrupted). Bust of Hermaeus r., diad.	ᵀᵖꓩ∧Ꮯꓕ ꓕꓕ ᏂᏃ⁻ᴶᎩ Ꮒ ᵀᏟ╫ᘁᏃ [ᒍᏃ] (*Kujula-kasasa kushaṇa yavu*(?)*gasa dhra-*(*dha*)*maṭhidasa*). Herakles, facing, diad.; holds in r. hand, club; in l., lion's skin.
11	Æ ·9		lower line of inscr. ΖΑΕΟΥ	
12	Æ ·9		inscr. retrograde.	inscr. varied. [Pl. xxv. 2.]
13	Æ ·9		inscr. retrograde and barbarous.	,, ,,
14	Æ 1·		twice struck.	inscr. varied ; in field, ᏊᎩ.
15	Æ ·8		degraded copy.	degraded copy.
16	Æ ·75		,,	
17	Æ ·85		,,	
18	Æ ·7		,,	
19	Æ ·7		,,	
20	Æ ·6		,,	
21	Æ ·6		,,	

KADPHISES I.

(a) Copper; type, Herakles.

No.	Wt.	Metal. Size.	Obverse.	Reverse.
			Inscr. as below. Bust of Hermaeus r., diad.	(*Kujula-kasasa kushaṇayavugasa dhra(dha)-maṭhidasa*). Herakles, facing, diad.; holds in r. hand, club; in l., lion's skin.
1		Æ ·95	KOPCNΛKOZOVΛO-KAΔΦIZOV	in field, [symbols]. [I. O. C. Pl. xxv. 3.]
2		Æ ·95	KOZOVΛOKAΔΦI-ZOV	[I. O. C.] (inscr. varied).
3		Æ ·9	KOPOИΛKOZOVΛO	„ [symbols]. [Pl. xxv. 4.]
4		Æ ·85	ИOKAΔΦICHOH	„ [symbol]. (inscr. varied).
5		Æ ·9	AΔΦIΣ	„ uncertain letter. „ „
6		Æ ·9	ΦIZOVKOΛC	„ [symbols].
7		Æ ·9	K..ZOYΛOKAΔ ZV	„ [symbols]. [I. O. C.]
8		Æ ·85	inscr. blundered.	„ [symbol]. [I. O. C.]

No.	Wt.	Metal. Size.	Obverse.	Reverse.
				## KADAPHES. (a) *Bronze; type of rev., king seated.*
			XOPANCY ZAOOY* **KOZOΛΛ KAΔA-** **ΦEC** Head of the king r., diad. (closely resembling that of Augustus).	 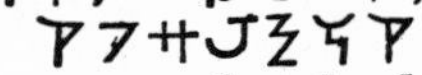 ꓨꓒꓱ ꓒꓥꓜ ꓨꓚꓚꓥ ꓨꓚꓕꓨ ꓨꓨ� ꓴꓜꓠꓨꓗ ꓨ (*Khushanasa yauasa kuyula kaphsasa sacha- dhramaṭhidasa*). The king seated r. on seat like curule chair; his r. hand extended; in field l., ꓕ.
1	Æ ·8			[Pl. xxv. 5.]
2	Æ ·7			
3	Æ ·7			
4	Æ ·7			[I. O. C.]
5	Æ ·7			[I. O. C.]
6	Æ ·7			[I. O. C.]
7	Æ ·75			
8	Æ ·7			to r., **Z**. [I. O. C.]
9	Æ ·7			,, ,,
10	Æ ·7			,, ,,
11	Æ ·65		barbarous inscr.; head l.	barbarous. [I. O. C.]

* The first O in **ZAOOY** has been read as a ☉; but wrongly, as is shewn by the corresponding Sanskrit form *yauasa*.

No.	Wt.	Metal. Size.	Obverse.	Reverse.
			### KADPHISES II. (a) *Gold ; type, figure or head of king.* BACIΛEYCOOH MO-KAΔΦICHC The king, wearing helmet and diadem, seated facing on throne; head turned to l. ; flames ascend from his shoulders ;* in his right a branch; beneath his feet a footstool; to r., 卐.	Ψ⌐ॻॻ ΨΥ⅂ॻ⅄Υॻ ΨΥ⅄∽ Ψ⅂Γᐟ⌖∪ ΨΥ⅂ᐞॻ ⅂⅃∿ ΨⱭⱮ⌧ᕼ∪⌖ (*Maharajasa rajadirajasa, sarvaloga iṣvarasa mahiṣvarasa hi(†)makapiṣasa tradata*). Siva facing, head l. ; holds trident in r. hand ; drapery over l. arm and hanging at back ; flames rising from head ; behind him, humped bull r. ; to l., ᕼ.
1	244·2	N ·95	to l., club.	[I. O. C. Pl. xxv. 6.]
			Same inscr. The king, wearing helmet and diadem, seated facing, cross-legged, on clouds ; head turned to r. ; in his r. is a club ; his head is surmounted by a trident ; to l., 卐.	Similar.
2	245·	N 1·		[Pl. xxv. 7.]
			Same inscr. Upper part of the king r., emerging from clouds ; wears helmet and diadem, and Greek chlamys ; club in r. hand ; to l., 卐.	Same inscr. (*i* of *iṣvarasa* wanting). Siva facing, wears headdress and drapery over shoulder ; holds trident in r. hand ; behind him bull r. ; to l., ᕼ.
3	122·4	N ·75		

* This is so usual on the gold coins of this king, that it will be omitted in subsequent descriptions.

† This letter looks on the coins rather like *tri* or *dri* than *hi*.

No.	Wt.	Metal. Size.	Obverse.	Reverse.
			BACIΛEYCOOH MO-KAΔΦICHC Similar, king wears diadem, but not helmet.	ᔨᐴ ᔨᐴ ᐴᔨ (*Maharajasa rajadirajasa, sarvaloga isvarasa mahisvarasa himakapisasa tradata*), last letters obscure. Siva facing, wears headdress and drapery over shoulder; holds trident in r. hand; behind him bull r.; to l., ☿.
4	123·2	*N* ·75		[I. O. C. Pl. xxv. 8.]
			Similar.	Same inscr. (last letters obscure). Siva facing, head l.; holds in r. hand, trident and battle-axe combined; in l., gourd; tiger-skin on l. arm; hair arranged in spiral form; to l., ☵; to r., ☿.
5	120·	*N* ·7		[I. O. C.]
			Same inscr. Upper part of the king l., emerging from clouds, wears diadem and helmet surmounted by trident; holds in r. hand, club; in l., elephant-goad; to r., ☵.	Similar.
6	122·	*N* ·75		[I. O. C. Pl. xxv. 9.]
7	121·2	*N* ·7		
			Same inscr. Upper part of the king r., emerging from clouds, wears diadem and helmet surmounted by trident; holds in r. hand, club; to l., ☵.	Similar.
8	121·2	*N* ·85		[I. O. C.]
9	122·4	*N* ·8		

No.	Wt.	Metal. Size.	Obverse.	Reverse.
			BACIΛEYCOOH[MO-KAΔΦICHC Head of king r., wearing helmet and diadem; within square frame.	ꝑꞨꞶ ꭒ꭪ ꞩꞶꞥꝯꞥꞶꞥ∼ꭒ (*Maharaja rajadiraja hima kapiṣasa*). Trident and battle-axe combined; to l., ꞩ; to r., ꞩ .
10	30·5	*N* ·45		[Pl. xxv. 10.]
			(β) *Silver; type, king standing.*	
			BACIΛEVC BACI-ΛEⲰN MEΓAC OOHMO KAΔΦI-CHC The king standing l., wearing diadem and helmet, sacrificing at altar; to l., trident and axe combined; to r., club and ꞩ .	ꝑꞨꞥꝑ ꞩꞶꞥꞥꝯꞩꝯꞶꝑꞶꞥ∼ꭒ ꝑꞨꞶ ꞩ ꭒ꭪ Ꞷꞥꞽ꭪ꭒ Ꞷꞥꞽꝯ ꞶꞞꞷ (*Maharajasa rajadirajasa sarvaloga iṣvara mahiṣvara himakapiṣasa tradata*). Siva facing; wears headdress and drapery over shoulder; holds trident in r. hand; behind him, bull r.
11	56·5	*Æ* 7		[I. O. C. Pl. xxv. 11.]
			[This coin, which is quite genuine, is the only known specimen of the class in silver.]	
			(γ) *Copper; type, king standing.*	
			[Inscription on both sides varied and incomplete in various specimens.]	
			BACIΛEVC BACI-ΛEⲰN CⲰTHP MEΓAC OOHMO KAΔΦICHC The king l., sacrificing at altar; to l., trident and axe combined; to r., club and ꞩ .	ꝑꞨꞥꝑ ꞶꞥꞥꞽꞥꞶ ꝑꞥꞶ∼ꭒ ꝑꞶꞽ꭪ꭒ ꝑꞶꞥꝯ ꞶꞞꞷ ꝑꞨꞶ ꭒ꭪ (*Maharajasa rajadirajasa, sarvaloga iṣvarasa mahiṣvarasa himakapiṣasa tradata*). Siva facing, holding trident; drapery hanging at his back; behind him, bull; to l., ꞩ .
12		*Æ* 1·1		[I. O. C. Pl. xxv. 12.]
13		*Æ* 1·1		,,

No.	Wt.	Metal. Size.	Obverse.	Reverse.
			BACIΛEVC BACI-ΛEⲰN CⲰTHP MEΓAC OOHMO KAΔΦICHC The king l., sacrificing at altar; to l., trident and axe combined; to r., club and 𝗆 .	Ψᛈᗱᛈ ᛈᎽᎽᏉᎽᎽ ᛈᎽᎽᏉᎽᎽ ᛈᎽᏒᕁᖑ ᛈᎽᏒᖟ ᎽᏃᏃ ᛈᎽᎽᖟᎽᖱᎽᕁᖱ (Maha-rajasa rajadirajasa, sarvaloga iṣ-varasa mahiṣvarasa himakapiṣasa tradata). Siva facing, holding trident; drapery hanging at his back; behind him, bull; to l., ᛞ .
14		Æ 1·05		[I. O. C]
15		Æ 1·1		,,
16		Æ 1·1		,,
17		Æ 1·05		
18		Æ 1·25	(twice struck).	
19		Æ 1·		
20		Æ 1·05		
21		Æ 1·1		
22		Æ 1·05		
23		Æ 1·15		
24		Æ 1·15		
25		Æ 1·1		
26		Æ 1·		in inscr. ᛈᎽᎽᏃᕁ between second and third words.

No.	Wt.	Metal. Size.	Obverse.	Reverse.
			ΒΑΣΙΛΕΥΣ ΒΑΣΙ-ΛΕΩΝ ΣΩΤΗΡ ΜΕΓΑΣ ΟΟΗΜΟ ΚΑΔΦΙΣΗΣ The king l., sacrificing at altar; to l., trident and axe combined; to r., club and ☗.	ꗪ (Maha-rajasa rajadirajasa, sarvaloga is-varasa mahisvarasa himakapisasa tradata). Siva facing, holding trident; drapery hanging at his back; behind him, bull; to l., ꖀ
27	Æ ·85			[Pl. xxv. 13.]
28	Æ ·65			[I. O. C. Pl. xxv. 14.]
29	Æ ·75			[I. O. C.]
30	Æ ·7			
31	Æ ·75			
32	Æ ·7			
33	Æ ·7			
34	Æ ·7			
35	Æ ·7			in place of inscr., fillet-border.

No.	Wt.	Metal. Size.	Obverse.	Reverse.

KANERKES.

(a) Gold; inscription, βασιλεὺς βασιλέων.

No.	Wt.	Metal. Size.	Obverse.	Reverse.
1	121·8	AV ·8	BACIΛEYC BACIΛEWN KANHPKOY The king l., wearing helmet and diadem, clad in coat and trousers, and cloak, sacrificing at altar; flames rise from shoulders; holds in l. hand, spear.	CAΛHNH Selene * (male) l., diad., clad in chiton and himation; crescent behind shoulders; r. hand advanced; holds in l. long sceptre, bound with fillet; sword girt round waist; to l., ⛣. [I. O. C. Pl. xxvi. 1.]

(β) Bronze; inscription, βασιλεὺς βασιλέων.

No.	Wt.	Metal. Size.	Obverse.	Reverse.
2		Æ ·9	BACIΛEYC BACIΛEWN KANHPKOY The king as above.	HΛIOC Helios l., diad., clad in chiton and himation; radiate disk behind head; r. hand advanced; l. on hip; to l., ⛣. [I. O. C. Pl. xxvi. 2.]
3		Æ ·9		
4		Æ ·9		
5		Æ ·9	Similar.	NANAIA Nanaia r., nimbate and diad.; holds in r. hand sceptre ending in forepart of horse; to r., ⛣. [I. O. C. Pl. xxvi. 3.]
6		Æ ·9		,,
7		Æ ·9		,,
8		Æ ·85		
9		Æ ·9		

* The figure of Selene is identical with that which appears on the coin inscribed MAO; it is that of a male moon-deity.

No.	Wt.	Metal. Size.	Obverse.	Reverse.
			(γ) *Gold ; inscription,* **PAONANO** &c.	
			PAONANOPAOKA NHPKIKOPANO The king standing l., wearing helmet and diadem, clad in coat and trousers, and cloak ; flames rise from his shoulders ; he holds in r. hand elephant-goad over altar ; in his l., spear ; sword at his waist.	**AΘPO** Bearded deity, fire-god, l., diad., clad in chiton and himation ; holds in r. hand, wreath ; in l., which rests on hip, tongs ; to l., ⛢ .
10	122·8	A′ ·8		[Pl. xxvi. 4.]
11	121·9	A′ ·75		
12	27·7	A′ ·5		[I. O. C. Pl. xxvi. 5.]
13	122·8	A′ ·8	Similar.	**APΔOXPO** Female figure r., wearing modius and nimbate, clad in chiton and himation ; holds cornucopiae ; to r., ⛢ . [Pl. xxvi. 6.]
14	120·2	A′ ·75	Similar.	**APOOACΠO** Bearded deity r., diad., clad in sleeved tunic ; holds in r. hand, wreath ; beside him, horse r., saddled, trotting ; to l., ⛢ . [Pl. xxvi. 7.]
15	122·	A′ ·75	(same die).	(same die). [I. O. C.]
16	109·2	A′ ·8	Similar.	**BOΔΔO** Buddha, facing, nimbate, clad in chiton and himation ; r. hand advanced ; in l., wallet ; to r., ⛢ . [I. O. C. Pl. xxvi. 8.]

No.	Wt.	Metal. Size.	Obverse.	Reverse.
			PAONANOPAOKA NhPKIKOPANO The king standing l., wearing helmet and diadem, clad in coat and trousers, and cloak; flames rise from his shoulders; he holds in r. hand elephant-goad over altar; in his l., spear; sword at his waist.	**MAO** Male deity (moon-god) l., diad., clad in chiton and himation; crescent behind shoulders; r. hand advanced; holds in l., long sceptre, bound with fillet; sword girt round waist; to l., ꙮ.
17	121 9	N ·75		[Pl. xxvi. 9.]
18	122·3	N ·8		(no sword).
19	118·	N ·8	Similar.	**MEIPO** Mithras, diad. and with radiate disk, to l.; r. hand advanced; in l., sceptre bound with fillet; sword girt round waist; to l., ꙮ.
20	122·3	N ·8	Similar.	**MIIPO** Mithras, to l.; r. hand advanced; l. rests on hip; sword at waist; to l. ꙮ. [Pl. xxvi. 10.]
21	123·2	N ·8	Similar.	**NANA** Nanaia r., nimbate and diad., head surmounted by crescent; holds sceptre ending in forepart of horse, and patera; to r., ꙮ.
22	120·3	N ·75	Similar.	**NANAPAO** Similar figure of Nanaia; to r., ꙮ.
23	122·2	N ·75		(sword at waist). [Pl. xxvi. 11.]
24	30·2	N ·5		„ „ [I. O. C. Pl. xxvi. 12.]

No.	Wt.	Metal. Size.	Obverse.	Reverse.
			PAONANOPAOKA NHPKIKOPANO The king standing l., wearing helmet and diadem, clad in coat and trousers, and cloak; flames rise from his shoulders; he holds in r. hand elephant-goad over altar; in his l., spear; sword at his waist.	**OKPO** Siva l., nimbate; hair in horn on top of head; has four arms and hands, in which he holds respectively a vase, a drum, a trident, and a goat, the last by the horns; to l., 〼.
25	123·	N ·8		[Pl. xxvi. 13.]
26	123·4	N ·75		[I. O. C.]
27	122·	N ·75		,,
28	29·	N ·5		[I. O. C. Pl. xxvi. 14.]
			Similar.	**OPΛAΓNO** War-god (Bahram?) r., wearing diadem, helmet surmounted by eagle, and clad like the king; holds in r. hand, spear; in l., sword; to r., 〼.
29	121·3	N ·85		[Pl. xxvi. 15.]
			Similar.	**ΦAPPO** Male figure to r., diad. and nimbate, clad in chiton and himation; holds spear in l. hand, and mountain or fire in r.; to r., 〼.
30	122·8	N ·8		[Pl. xxvi. 16.]
			PAONANOKANHP KI KOPANO Bust of the king l., diad. and wearing helmet; l. hand raised, holds spear; body emerges from clouds.	**AΘPO** Bearded deity l., clad in chiton and himation; holds in r. hand wreath; in l., which rests on hip, tongs; to l., 〼.
31	30·8	N ·5		[I. O. C. Pl. xxvi. 17.]
			Similar.	**OKPO** Siva, as above, not nimbate; to l. 〼.
32	30·1	N ·5		[Pl. xxvi. 18.]

No.	Wt.	Metal. Size.	Obverse.	Reverse.
			Later period.	
			PAO NANOPA[O [KA]NHPKOKOPANO The king standing l. at altar, nimbate; holds r. hand over altar; in l., spear bound with fillet; to l., trident bound with fillet.	**A]PΔOKPO** Goddess, seated facing on throne, nimbate; under feet, footstool; holds wreath and cornucopiae to l., ⚇.
33	30·6	𝒩 ·5		[I. O. C. Pl. xxvi. 19.]
			(δ) *Bronze; inscr.* **PAO** &c.	
			PAOKA NHPKI The king, clad as in last class, standing l. by altar; holds in l. hand spear; r. extended over altar.	**AΘPO** Bearded deity l.; holds in r. hand, wreath; in l., which rests on hip, tongs(?); to l., ⚇.
34		Æ 1·05		[Pl. xxvii. 1.]
35		Æ 1·		
36		Æ 1·05	inscr. barbarous.	
			Similar.	**OΔYOBOY** Buddha facing, nim- **CAKAMA** bate; his r. hand raised as in teaching; in l., wallet; to l., ⚇.
37		Æ ·85		[Pl. xxvii. 2.]
38		Æ ·9		[I. O. C.]
			Similar.	**MAO** Male deity l., clad as king; crescent behind shoulders; r. hand advanced; in l., long sceptre bound with fillet; sword at waist; to l., ⚇.
39		Æ 1·05	king nimbate; to l., ⚇.	[Pl. xxvii. 3.]
40		Æ 1·05		deity does not hold sceptre.
41		Æ ·85		

No.	Wt.	Metal. Size.	Obverse.	Reverse.
			PAOKA NHPKI The king standing l. as before; holds in l. hand spear; r. extended over altar.	**MAO** Male deity l., clad as king; crescent behind shoulders; r. hand advanced; in l., long sceptre bound with fillet; sword at waist; to l., ⛉.
42		Æ ·75	to l., ⅄. (inscr. retrogr.)	(inscr. retrogr.)
43		Æ ·75	„ „	deity does not hold sceptre.
44		Æ ·75	„ „	„ „ „
45		Æ ·5	„ „	„ „ „
			Similar.	**MIOPO** Sun-god, Mithras, l., diad. with radiate disk, clad as king; r. hand advanced; in l., sword; to l., ⛉.
46		Æ 1·05		[Pl. xxvii. 4.]
47		Æ 1·05		
48		Æ 1·		inscr. **MIIPO**.
49		Æ 1·1		„ „
50		Æ ·8		„ „
51		Æ ·85		
52		Æ ·65		
53		Æ ·7		inscr. **MIYPO**.
			Similar.	**NANA** Nanaia r., nimbate and diad.; holds sceptre, ending in forepart of horse, and patera; to r., ⛉.
54		Æ 1·05		[I. O. C. Pl. xxvii. 5.]
55		Æ ·95		
56		Æ 1·		

No.	Wt.	Metal. Size.	Obverse.	Reverse.
			PAOKA NHPKI The king standing l. by altar; holds in l. hand spear; r. extended over altar.	**NANA** Nanaia r., nimbate and diad.; holds sceptre, ending in forepart of horse, and patera; to r., �.
57		Æ ·7	to l., ↑.	
58		Æ ·7	,, ,,	
59		Æ ·7	,, ,,	
60		Æ ·55		
61		Æ ·6		
			Similar.	**OAΔO** Wind-god running l., his hair loose; holds in both hands ends of his garment which floats about him; to l., �.
62		Æ1·05		[I. O. C. Pl. xxvii. 6.]
63		Æ1·05		[I. O. C.]
64		Æ1·05		
65		Æ ·65		
			Similar.	**OKPO** Siva l., nimbate; has four arms and hands, in which he holds a wreath, a drum, a trident, and a vase; to l., �.
66		Æ 1·		[I. O. C.]
67		Æ 1·		
68		Æ ·8		
69		Æ ·8		[I. O. C. Pl. xxvii. 7.]
			Similar.	**OKPO** Siva l., nimbate; holds in r. hand, trident; to l., �.
70		Æ ·75	to l., ⅄.	
71		Æ ·75	,, ,,	(not nimbate).

No.	Wt.	Metal. Size.	Obverse.	Reverse.
				HOOERKES.
				(a) *Gold.*
			PAONANOPAOO Upper part of king l., emerging from clouds; is diad. and nimbate; wears conical helmet and coat of mail; holds ear of corn and spear.*	**AⴲOPO** Hephaestus standing r., flames rising from shoulders; holds hammer and tongs; to r., ⚹.
1	121·5	N ·8		[Pl. xxvii. 8.]
			PAONANOP AOOOᏂPKIKO Similar.	**AⴲPO** Similar.
2	123·5	N ·85		
			PAONANOPAOOO ᏂPKIKOPANO Similar.	Similar; symbol to l.
3	120·9	N ·85		
			Similar.	**APAЄIXPO** Sun-god l., diad. and with radiate disk; r. hand advanced, and two fingers raised; l. rests on hip; to l., ⚹.
4	123·5	N ·85		[Pl. xxvii. 9.]
5	122·8	N ·9		[I. O. C.]

* It has been judged unnecessary to describe at length the details of the king's costume in this and other coins.

No.	Wt.	Metal. Size.	Obverse.	Reverse.
			PAONANOPAO OO HPKIKOPANO Upper part of king l., emerging from clouds; diad. and nimbate; wears conical helmet and coat of mail; holds ear of corn and spear.	APΔOXPO Female deity r., in Greek attire; holds in both hands cornucopiae; to r., 米 .
6	124·5	AV ·8		[Pl. xxvii. 10.]
7	122·	AV ·85		
8	122·5	AV ·8		
9	122·4	AV ·8		to r., fire (?).
10	58·3 (plated)	AV ·8		
11	122·	AV ·85		inscr. APΔOXPA. [I. O. C.]
12	123·5	AV ·85		type l., and symbol to l. [I. O. C.]
13	30·6	AV ·55	inscr. PAONANO OOH	[I. O. C.]
			PAONANO PAOO OHPKIKOPANO Upper part of king l., emerging from clouds, diad.; wears rounded helmet; holds ear of corn and elephant-goad.	Similar.
14	122·5	AV ·85		deity with modius and nimbus.
15	120·7	AV ·8	inscr. OYOHPKI for OOHPKI.	inscr. OqOΔqA.
16	120·6	AV ·8		type l., and symbol to l.
17	30 6	AV ·5		deity with modius and nimbus. [Pl. xxvii. 11.]
			PAONANOPAO OOHPKOKOPANO The king r., riding on elephant; holds sceptre and elephant-goad.	Similar. Deity with modius and nimbus.
18	120·9	AV ·8		[Pl. xxvii. 12.]

T

No.	Wt.	Metal. Size.	Obverse.	Reverse.
			Inscr. obscure. Upper part of king l., emerging from clouds, diad.; wears rounded helmet; holds ear of corn and elephant-goad.	ΔOXPO Female figure l., nimbate; holds wreath and cornucopiae; to l., ⾺.
19	122·5	N ·8		[Pl. xxvii. 13.]
20	123·3	N ·8		
			PAONANOPAOOO ҺPKIKOPANO Upper part of the king l., emerging from clouds, diad. and nimbate; wears conical helmet and chlamys over armour; holds ear of corn and spear.	MIOPO Female deity r., diad. and nimbate, in Greek attire; holds cornucopiae in both hands; to r., ⾺.
21	123·	N ·8		[Pl. xxvii. 14.]
			PAONANOPA OOOҺPKI The king seated cross-legged to l., diad. and nimbate; flames rising from shoulders; wears conical helmet, and holds ear of corn and spear.	ҺPAPIΛO Bearded Heracles l., naked; holds in r. hand, club; over l. arm, lion's skin; in l. hand, apple; to l., ⾺.
22	123·3	N ·8		[Pl. xxvii. 15.]
			PAONANOPAOO OҺPKIKOPANO Upper part of the king l., emerging from clouds, diad.; wears rounded helmet; holds ear of corn and elephant-goad.	MAACҺNO Male deity (Mahásená) facing, nimbate and diad., clad in coat and chlamys; holds in r. hand, standard surmounted by bird; in l., sword; to l., ⾺.
23	125·5	N ·8		[I. O. C. Pl. xxvii. 16.]
24	112·7	N ·75		

No.	Wt.	Metal. Size.	Obverse.	Reverse.
			PAONANOPAOO OHPKIKOPANO Upper part of the king l., emerging from clouds, diad.; wears rounded helmet; holds ear of corn and elephant-goad.	**MANAOBAГO** Moon-god facing, seated on throne; feet resting on footstool; wears helmet; crescent behind shoulders; has four arms and hands, in three of which he grasps sceptre, wreath ? and fire ?, fourth hand rests on hip; to r., 米 .
25	122·	N ·75		[Pl. xxvii. 17.]
26	122·5	N ·8		
			PAONANOPAOO OHPKIKOPANO Upper part of the king l., emerging from clouds, diad. and nimbate; wears conical helmet and coat of mail; holds ear of corn and spear.	**MAO** Moon-god l., crescent behind shoulders; clad in coat; holds wreath and sceptre; sword at waist; to l., 米 .
27	122·3	N ·85		[Pl. xxvii. 18.]
			Similar.	**MAO** Moon-god l., crescent behind shoulders; clad in chiton and chlamys; sword in l.; holds wreath in r. hand; to l., 米 .
28	122·2	N ·85		
29	123·2	N ·8		[I. O. C.]
			Similar.	**MAO** Moon-god l.; holds sceptre in l.; r. hand advanced; to l., 米 .
30	122·6	N ·85		[I. O. C. Pl. xxvii. 19.]
			PAONANOP AOOOHPKO Similar type.	**MAO** Moon-god l.; r. hand extended; in l., sword; to l., 米 .
31	30·2	N ·5		[I. O. C. Pl. xxvii. 20.]

No.	Wt.	Metal. Size.	Obverse.	Reverse.
32	120·4	A̶ ·9	PAONANOPAOO OHPKIKOPANO Upper part of the king l., emerging from clouds, diad. ; wears rounded helmet, and chlamys over armour ; holds ear of corn and elephant-goad.	MAƆ Moon-god l. ; holds sceptre in l. hand ; to l., 峇 .
33	121·2	A̶ ·8	Similar.	MAO Moon-god l. ; holds sceptre in r. hand ; to l., 峇 . [Pl. xxvii. 21.]
34	122·5	A̶ ·8		[I. O. C.]
35	122·4	A̶ ·75	Similar.	MAO Moon-god l. ; r. hand extended ; in l., sceptre, held transversely ; to l., 峇 .
36	121·2	A̶ ·8		sceptre bound with fillet.
37	121·2	A̶ ·8		„ „ [Pl. xxvii. 22.]
38	123·	A̶ ·85		(inscr. MAOO).
39	122·8	A̶ ·85	Similar.	MAO Moon-god l. ; r. hand extended ; sword in l. ; to l., 峇 .
40	121·4	A̶ ·8		(inscr. MAOO).
41	122·	A̶ ·8	Similar.	MAO Moon-god r., diad. ; holds in r. hand, wreath ; in l., sceptre ; to r., 峇 . [Pl. xxvii. 23.]

No.	Wt.	Metal. Size.	Obverse.	Reverse.
42	121·1	N ·8	**PAONANOPAOO OHPKIKOPANO** Upper part of the king l., emerging from clouds, diad. ; wears rounded helmet, and chlamys over armour; holds ear of corn and elephant-goad.	Bearded moon-god r., diad.; crescent behind shoulders; holds in r. hand, sceptre, bound with fillet; in l., elephant-goad : and sun-god l., radiate ; r. hand advanced ; in l., sceptre, bound with fillet ; behind the two, the names **MAO** and **MIIPO** respectively ; between them, ⛩. [Pl. xxvii. 24.]
43	123·	N ·85	**PAONANOPAOOO HPKEKOPANO** Upper part of the king l., emerging from clouds, diad. and nimbate ; flames rising from shoulders ; wears conical helmet ; holds ear of corn and spear.	**MIIPO** Sun-god l., nimbate; holds wreath and sceptre ; sword at waist ; to l., ⛩.
44	122·3	N ·85		
45	123·	N ·8	Similar ; no flames.	**MOPO** Sun-god l., radiate ; holds wreath and sceptre ; sword at waist ; to l., ⛩. [Pl. xxviii. 1.]
46	121·7	N ·8	Similar.	**MIOPO** Sun-god l., radiate ; holds wreath and sceptre, bound with fillet ; to l., ⛩. [I. O. C.]
47	122·8	N ·8	Similar ; king holds standard instead of spear.	**MIOPO** Sun-god l., diad. and nimbate; holds wreath and sword; to l., ⛩.

No.	Wt.	Metal. Size.	Obverse.	Reverse.
48	122·2	A̅ ·9	**PAONANOPAOOO ҺPKIKOPANO** Upper part of the king l., emerging from clouds, diad. and nimbate; wears conical helmet; holds ear of corn and spear.	**MIYPO** Sun-god l., diad. and radiate; holds wreath and sword; to l., 𝍷.
49	121·3	A̅ ·85	Similar.	**MIIPO** Sun-god r., radiate; holds spear and sword; to r., 𝍷 . [I. O. C. Pl. xxviii. 2.]
50	30·2	A̅ ·5	**PAOOOҺ** Similar.	**MYPO** Sun-god l., nimbate; r. hand advanced; in l., sceptre; to l., 𝍷. [I. O. C. Pl. xxviii. 3.]
51	30·7	A̅ ·55	**PAONANOPA OOOҺPKI** Upper part of the king l., emerging from clouds, diad.; wears rounded helmet; holds ear of corn and elephant-goad.	**MIOPO** Sun-god l., radiate; holds wreath and sceptre; to l., 𝍷 . [I. O. C.]
52	120·8	A̅ ·8	**PAONANOPAOOY OҺPKIKOPANO** Similar.	**MIOPO** Sun-god l., radiate; r. hand holds spear; l. grasps sword; to l., 𝍷.
53	122·8	A̅ ·8		[I. O. C.]
54	122·2	A̅ ·85	**PAONANOPAO OOҺPKIKOPANO** Similar.	**MIOPO** Sun-god l., radiate; l. hand holds spear; r. rests on hip; sword at waist; to l., 𝍷 . [Pl. xxviii. 4.]

No.	Wt.	Metal. Size.	Obverse.	Reverse.
55	123·	N ·8	PAONANOPAO OOHPKIKOPANO Upper part of the king l., emerging from clouds, diad. ; wears rounded helmet ; holds ear of corn and elephant-goad.	MIIPO Sun-god l., radiate ; r. hand extended ; in l., sceptre, held transversely, bound with fillet ; to l., ☒.
56	121·4	N ·75		inscr. MIOPO.
57	120·8	N ·8	(bust only of king).	
58	120·	N ·8	„ „	[I. O. C.]
59	122·7	N ·8		inscr. MYPO. [I. O. C.]
60	30·2	N ·5		
61	29·5	N ·5		
62	120·6	N ·75	Similar.	MIPPO Sun-god l., radiate ; r. hand advanced ; l. holds sword ; to l., ☒.
63	122·3	N ·8		inscr. MIIPO. [I. O. C.]
64	119·5	N ·8		„ MIPO. „
65	118·	N ·8	Same inscr. Upper part of king as above, to r.	MIIPO Similar. [I. O. C.]
66	122·3	N ·85	Same inscr. Upper part of king as above, to l.	MIIPO Sun-god r., diad. and radiate ; holds wreath and sword ; to r., ☒.
67	122·4	N ·8		[Pl. xxviii. 5.]

No.	Wt.	Metal. Size.	Obverse.	Reverse.
			PAONANOPAO OOHPKIKOPANO Upper part of king l., emerging from clouds, diad. and nimbate; wears conical helmet; holds ear of corn and spear.	OΜΙΑ Sun-god advancing l., radiate; r. hand advanced; l. holds sword; to l., .
68	26·	AV ·5		
69	28·8	AV ·5		[I. O. C.]
70	30·2	AV ·55		[I. O. C. Pl. XXVIII. 6.]
			PAONANOPAOOO HPKEKOPANO Upper part of king l., emerging from clouds, diad. and nimbate; flames rise from shoulders; wears conical helmet; holds ear of corn and spear.	HPO (MEIPO?) Artemis standing r., clad in long chiton and himation; holds in l. hand, bow; and with r., draws arrow from quiver; to r., .
71	122·3	AV ·85		[Pl. XXVIII. 7.]
			PAONANOPAOOO HPKIKOPANO Upper part of king l., emerging from clouds, diad. and nimbate; wears conical helmet; holds ear of corn and spear.	NANA Nanaia l., wears stephane; holds sceptre, ending in forepart of horse, and patera; to l., .
72	121·7	AV ·8		[Pl. XXVIII. 8.]
			Similar.	NANO Nanaia r., diad. and nimbate; crescent on head; holds sceptre and patera; to r., .
73	124·	AV ·85		[I. O. C.]
74	123·	AV ·85	king's name OOHPKO.	inscr. NANA. [I. O. C.]
75	121·3	AV ·85	" OHPKO.	" "

No.	Wt.	Metal. Size.	Obverse.	Reverse.
			PAONANOPAOOO HPKIKOPANO Upper part of king l., emerging from clouds, diad. and nimbate; wears conical helmet; holds ear of corn and spear.	**NANO** Nanaia r., diad. and nimbate; crescent on head; holds sceptre and patera; to r., ⚊.
76	122·9	N ·8	king holds double ear of corn.*	[Pl. xxviii. 9.]
77	122·5	N ·85	king's name **OOHPKO**.	[I. O. C.]
78	121·2	N ·85	„ **OOHPKE**.	inscr. barbarous.
79	122·5	N ·8	„ „	„ „
80	122·6	N ·85	„ „	„ „ [I. O. C.]
			PAONANOPAOO OHPKOKOPANOPAO King seated cross-legged on clouds, head r., diad. and helmeted; holds in l., standard, surmounted by bird.	**NANA** Nanaia r., diad. and nimbate; crescent on head; sword at waist; holds sceptre and patera; to r., ⚌.
81	120·8	N ·85		
82	119·5	N ·8		[I. O. C. Pl. xxviii. 10.]
			PAONANOPAOO OHPKIKOPANO Upper part of the king l., emerging from clouds, diad.; wears rounded helmet; holds ear of corn and elephant-goad.	**NANAPAO** Nanaia r., diad. and nimbate; crescent on head; sword at waist; holds sceptre and patera; to r., ⚊.
83	118·8	N ·8		
84	121·3	N ·8		[I. O. C.]

* This specimen proves that the object in the king's r. hand is an ear of corn, and not a club as it has usually been supposed to be.

No.	Wt.	Metal. Size.	Obverse.	Reverse.
			PAONANOPAOO OHPKIKOPANO Upper part of the king l., emerging from clouds, diad. : wears rounded helmet ; holds ear of corn and elephant-goad.	**NANA** Nanaia r., diad. and nimbate ; crescent on head ; sword at waist ; holds sceptre and patera ; to r., 关 .
85	122·4	N ·8		[I. O. C.]
86	122·	N ·8		
87	119·7	N ·8		
88	121·4	N ·8		inscr. **NANO** .
			Similar.	**NANA** Nanaia l., diad. and nimbate ; crescent on head ; holds sceptre in outstretched r. hand ; in l., patera ; to l., 关 .
89	121·6	N ·85		[I. O. C.]
90	120·	N ·8		inscr. **NANO** . [I. O. C. Pl. xxviii. 11.]
91	122·4	N ·8		,,　　,,
92	121·2	N ·8		,,　　,,
93	121·1	N ·85	inscr. barbarous.	inscr. barbarous.
			Similar.	**OΔIIO** Nanaia r., diad. and nimbate ; holds sceptre, bound with fillet, and patera ; to r., 关 .
94	119·6	N ·85		[Pl. xxviii. 12.]

No.	Wt.	Metal. Size.	Obverse.	Reverse.
			PAONANOPAOOO ҺPKEKOPANO Upper part of king l., emerging from clouds, diad. and nimbate; wears conical helmet; flames rising from shoulders; holds ear of corn and spear.	OANINΔA Nike standing l.; holds wreath and trophy-stand, as on coins of Alexander; to r., ⛎.
95	122·	N· ·85		[Pl. xxviii. 13.]
96	121·7	N· ·8		inscr. OANINΔO.
			PAONANOPAOO OҺPKIKOPANO Upper part of king l., emerging from clouds, diad.; flames rising from shoulders; wears rounded helmet; holds ear of corn and ele-phant-goad.	OKPO Siva l., nimbate; wears necklace, and has four arms and hands, in which are (1) vase and elephant-goad, (2) thunderbolt, (3) trident, (4) goat; to l., ⛎.
97	122·7	N· ·8		[Pl. xxviii. 14.]
98	121·5	N· ·8		[I. O. C.]
99	120·1	N· ·8		
			Inscr. barbarous. Similar	OKPO Siva l., with four arms and hands, in which are (1) wreath, (2) ?, (3) trident, (4) goat; to l., ⛎.
100	123·	N· ·85		
			PAONANOPA OOҺPK Upper part of king l., emerging from clouds, diad. and nimbate; wears rounded helmet; holds ear of corn and standard sur-mounted by bird.	OKPA Siva facing, three-headed; has four arms and hands, in which are vase, thunderbolt, trident, and club; to l., ⛎.
101	122·2	N· ·85		[Pl. xxviii. 15.]

No.	Wt.	Metal. Size.	Obverse.	Reverse.
			PAONANOPA OOOHPKIKOPANO Upper part of the king l., emerging from clouds, diad. and nimbate; wears conical helmet; holds ear of corn and spear.	OKPO Siva facing, three-headed, nimbate; clad only in waistband, ithyphallic; has four arms and hands, in which are goat, wheel, trident, and thunderbolt; to r., ☧.
102	123·5	N ·85		[Pl. xxviii. 16.]
			Similar.	PAOPHOPO Ares standing r., in Greek helmet and armour; holds spear, and shield which rests on ground; to r., ☧.
103	123·	N ·8		[Pl. xxviii. 17.]
104	121·7	N ·8	inscr. barbarous.	inscr. VAOPHOO. [I. O. C.]
105	122·5	N ·85	(last letters of inscr. wanting).	
			PAONANOPAOO OHPKOK Similar type.	PAOPHOAP Similar.
106	122·8	N ·85		
			PAONANOPAOOO HPKEKOPANO Similar type.	PAOPHOPO Ares l., in Greek helmet and armour; holds shield in r. hand, spear in l.; to l, ☧.
107	122·5	N ·85		[Pl. xxviii. 18.]
			Same inscr. Upper part of king, as above; holds ear of corn and sceptre.	PAOPHOPO Ares r., in Greek helmet and armour, nimbate; holds spear and sword; to l, ☧.
108	123·	N ·8		[Pl. xxviii. 19.]

No.	Wt.	Metal. Size.	Obverse.	Reverse.
			Inscr. obscure. Upper part of king l., emerging from clouds, diad. ; wears rounded helmet ; holds ear of corn and elephant-goad.	PIDM Roma or Pallas standing r., wearing helmet and long chiton; holds spear and shield; to r., 쓩.
109	123·5	Ν ·85		[Pl. xxviii. 20.]
			PAONANOPA OOYOHPKIKOP Similar.	CAPAΠO Sarapis standing l., diad. and clad in himation ; r. hand advanced ; in l., sceptre ; to l., 犬.
110	123·1	Ν ·85		[Pl. xxviii. 21.]
111	121·6	Ν ·85		[I. O. C.]
			PAONANOPAOO OHPKIKOPANO Upper part of king l., emerging from clouds, diad. ; wears rounded helmet ; holds ear of corn and elephant-goad.	CKANΔOKO M BIZAΓO APO Skanda and Viṣākha* standing face to face, nimbate ; each wearing chlamys and necklace, and sword at waist; but Skanda holds in r. hand, standard surmounted by bird ; Viṣākha holds in l. hand, spear; between them, 쓩.
112	123·	Ν ·8		[Pl. xxviii. 22.]
113	121·3	Ν ·8		
			Similar; last letter of inscr. wanting.	CKANΔOKOMAPO B IZAΓO Skanda and Viṣākha standing face to face, nimbate; Skanda holds in r. hand, standard; Viṣākha holds in l. hand, spear; between them, 犬.
114	31·	Ν ·5		[I. O. C. Pl. xxviii. 23.]

* A son and impersonation of Skanda. *See* Introduction.

No.	Wt.	Metal. Size.	Obverse.	Reverse.
115	121·	N ·8	**PAONANOPAOO OHPKIKOPANO** Upper part of king l., emerging from clouds, diad. ; wears rounded helmet ; holds ear of corn and elephant-goad.	**CKANΔOK OMAPOMA AC H NOBIZAГO** Niche on basis, within which, Skanda and Viśā-kha standing as above ; between them, Mahāsena, horned(?), facing, nimbate, clad in chlamys ; sword at waist ; to l., 米 . [Pl. xxviii. 24.]
116	123·2	N ·8	**PAONANPAOO OHKIKOPANO** Upper part of king l., emerging from clouds, diad. and nimbate ; wears conical helmet ; holds ear of corn and spear.	**ΦAPPO** Male deity l., head winged ; clad in coat ; holds in r. hand, fire ; l. grasps sword at waist ; to l., 米 . [I. O. C. Pl. xxviii. 25.]
117	122·4	N ·85	**HPKIKOPANO** Upper part of king l., emerging from clouds, diad. and nimbate ; flames rise from shoul-ders ; wears conical hel-met ; holds ear of corn and standard.	**ΦAPPO** Male deity l., head winged, diad. ; flames rising from shoul-ders ; wears coat and chlamys ; holds in r. hand, fire ; l. grasps sword at waist ; to l., 米 .
118	121·6	N ·8	**PAONANOPAO OOHPKIKOPANO** Upper part of king l., emerging from clouds, diad. and nimbate ; wears conical helmet ; holds ear of corn and standard surmounted by bird.	**ΦAPPO** Similar ; deity nimbate.

No.	Wt.	Metal. Size.	Obverse.	Reverse
			PAONANOPAOOO hPKIKOPANO King as last ; holding ear of corn and spear.	ΦAPO Male deity l., head winged, nimbate ; wears coat and chlamys ; r. hand advanced ; in l., long sceptre ; sword at waist ; to l., ⛏.
119	123·4	N ·8		[I. O. C.]
			Same inscr. King as last ; holding ear of corn and sceptre.	ΦAPPO Male deity l., nimbate ; flames rising from shoulders ; holds in extended r. hand, fire ; in l., sceptre ; to l., ⛏.
120	121·2	N ·8		[Pl. xxviii. 26.]
			Same inscr. King as before ; holding ear of corn and spear.	ΦAPPO Male deity r., head winged, nimbate ; clad in coat ; holds sceptre and fire ; to r., ⛏.
121	123·3	N ·8		[Pl. xxviii. 27.]
			Same inscr.? King as before ; holding double ear of corn and spear.	ΦAPPO Male deity l., head winged, nimbate ; clad in coat and chlamys ; holds purse and caduceus ; to l., ⛏.
122	122·4	N ·8		[I. O. C.]
			PAONANOPA OOOhPKEKOPA King as before ; holding ear of corn and spear.	ΦAPO Similar figure ; holds purse ? and long sceptre ; to l., ⛏.
123	123·5	N ·8		[Pl. xxviii. 28.]
			PAONANOPAOOO hPKIKOPANO Similar.	ΦAPPO Male deity r., head winged, diad. and nimbate ; clad in coat ; holds sceptre and elephant-goad ; to l., ⛏.
124	121·5	N ·8		[Pl. xxviii. 29.]

No.	Wt.	Metal. Size.	Obverse.	Reverse.
			ΡΑΟΝΑΝΟΡΑΟ ΟΟΗΡΚΟΚΟΡ Upper part of king l., emerging from clouds, diad. and nimbate; wears rounded helmet; holds ear of corn and standard.	Inscr. barbarous. Male deity l., nimbate; in extended r. hand, fire; in l., sword; to l., [monogram].
125	124·1	AV ·85		
			ΡΑΟΝΑΝΟΡΑΟΟ ΟΗΡΚΙΚΟΡΑΝΟ Upper part of king l., emerging from clouds, diad.; wears rounded helmet; holds ear of corn and elephant-goad.	ΦΑΡΟ Male deity l., head winged, nimbate; holds in r. hand, wreath; in l., sceptre; to l., [monogram].
126	121·2	AV ·8		
			Similar.	ΦΑΡΡΟ Male deity r., head winged, nimbate; r. hand rests on hip; in l., sceptre; to r., [monogram].
127	122·5	AV ·75		
128	121·7	AV ·8		[I. O. C.]
129	122·2	AV ·9		inscr. ΦΑΡΟ.
130	33·3	AV ·5		
131	27·	AV ·5		[I. O. C. Pl. XXVIII. 30.]
			Similar	ΦΑΡΟ Male deity l.; l. hand rests on hip; in r., sceptre; to l., [monogram].
132	123·3	AV ·75		
133	121·4	AV ·8		inscr. ΦΑΡΡΟ. [I. O. C.]
134	122·1	AV ·8		„ ΟϘΑΦ. (sword at waist).

No.	Wt.	Metal. Size.	Obverse.	Reverse.
135	120·8	*N* ·8	**PAONANOPAOO OHPKIKOPANO** Upper part of king l., emerging from clouds, diad. ; wears rounded helmet ; holds ear of corn and elephant-goad.	**ΦΑΡΟ** Male deity l., head winged, nimbate, standing on fire ; holds in r. hand, fire ; in l., sceptre ; to l., ᛩ.
136	120·	*N* ·8	Similar.	**ΦΑΡΡΟ** Male deity l., head winged, nimbate, standing on fire ; r. hand extended ; in l., caduceus ; to l., 米.
137	122·4	*N* ·8		[I. O. C. Pl. xxviii. 31.]
138	122·	*N* ·8	Similar.	**ωPON** Male deity l., bearded, wearing modius and himation ; r. hand advanced ; in l., long sceptre ; to l., 米. [Pl. xxviii. 32.]
139	122·2	*N* ·8		[I. O. C.]

(β) *Bronze ; type, King on elephant.*

No.	Wt.	Metal. Size.	Obverse.	Reverse.
140		Æ 1·	**PAONANO PAOOO-HPKENOPANO** * The king r., diad. and nimbate, riding on elephant ; holds spear and elephant-goad.	**AΘPO** Male deity l., diad. ; holds in r. hand, wreath ; and in l., tongs ; to l., ᛩ.
141		Æ1·15		
142		Æ 1·		

* This inscription cannot be read entire on any single specimen ; and many specimens are blundered or barbarous : but the formula in the text seems to be the normal and usual one.

x

No.	Wt.	Metal. Size.	Obverse.*	Reverse.
			PAONANO PAOOO-ⲎPKENOPANO The king r., diad. and nimbate, riding on elephant; holds spear and elephant-goad.	APOOXP Female deity r., diad. and nimbate; holds cornucopiae; to r., ⚍.
143		Æ 1·		
144		Æ ·95		[I. O. C.]
			Similar.	Inscr. obscure. Female deity * l., nimbate; holds in extended r. hand, wreath; in l., cornucopiae; to l., ⚍.
145		Æ 1·		[I. O. C.]
			Similar.	HPAKΛO? Heracles r.; holds in r. hand, club; l. raised to head; to r., ⚍.
146		Æ ·95		[Pl. xxix. 1.]
			Similar.	MAO Moon-god l., crescent behind shoulders; r. hand extended; with l. grasps sword; to l., ⚍.
147		Æ 1·05		[I. O. C. Pl. xxix. 2.]
148		Æ 1·		
149		Æ 1·		
150		Æ 1·		
151		Æ ·85		
152		Æ ·8		(deity holds wreath and sword).

* Cf. the deity accompanied by the inscription ΔOXPO on gold of this king.

No.	Wt.	Metal. Size.	Obverse.	Reverse.
153		Æ 1·05	**PAONANO PAOOO-hPKENOPANO** The king r., diad. and nimbate, riding on elephant; holds spear and elephant-goad.	**MAO** Female deity l., nimbate; holds in both hands, cornucopiae; to l., [symbol].
154		Æ 1·	Similar.	**MIIOPO** Sun-god l., radiate; r. hand extended; with l. grasps sword; to l., [symbol]. [I. O. C.]
155		Æ 1·		(inscr. **MIIPO**).
156		Æ ·95		„ „
157		Æ 1·	Barbarous inscr. King on elephant to l.	**MPPO**? Sun-god l., nimbate; r. hand extended; in l., sceptre; to l., [symbol].
158		Æ 1·05	**PAONANO PAOOO-hPKENOPANO** The king r., diad. and nimbate, riding on elephant; holds spear and elephant-goad.	**OKPO** Siva standing l., four armed; holds wreath, thunderbolt, trident, and goat; to l., [symbol].
159		Æ 1·		(Siva holds in fourth hand, vase). [Pl. xxix. 3.]
160		Æ 1·05	Similar.	**OKPO** Siva standing l., two armed; holds in r. hand, trident; in l., vase and lion's skin (?); to l., [symbol]; to r., [symbol].
161		Æ 1·		
162		Æ ·9		[I. O. C.]
163		Æ ·85		
164		Æ ·95		
165		Æ ·95		

No.	Wt.	Metal. Size.	Obverse.	Reverse.
			(γ) *Bronze ; type, King seated.*	
166		Æ 1·	PAONANOPAO OOHPKENOPANO* King facing, head r., seated cross-legged on cushions, body radiate ; in l. hand, sceptre.	AΘPO Male deity l.; holds wreath in extended r. hand; to l., ⛎.
167		Æ 1·	Inscr. King, head and body radiate, seated facing on throne.	Similar.
168		Æ 1·		
169		Æ ·8	Inscr. King nimbate, facing, head r., seated ; holds in l. hand, sceptre.	APΔOXP Female deity l. ; holds cornucopiae; to l., ⛎.
170		Æ ·8	Inscr. King nimbate, r., reclining.	AP]ΔOXP Female deity l. ; holds in r. hand, sceptre (?); to l., ⛎.
171		Æ 1·	Inscr. King seated cross-legged on cushions, facing, head r., head and body radiate ; l. hand raised.	MAO Moon-god l., crescent behind shoulders ; r. hand advanced ; with l. grasps sword ; to l., ⛎. [I. O. C. Pl. xxix. 4.]
172		Æ 1·	in l., sceptre.	
173		Æ 1·	,, ,,	
174		Æ ·95	,, ,,	
175		Æ ·8	,, ,,	

* On coins of this class the inscription is even more debased than on those of the last; sometimes, however, it ends OOHPKEKOPANO .

No.	Wt.	Metal. Size.	Obverse.	Reverse.
			PAONANOPAO OOHPKENOPANO King seated cross-legged, facing, head r., nimbate ; holds in each hand, staff or sword.	**MAO** Moon-god l., crescent behind shoulders ; r. hand advanced ; with l. grasps sword ; to l., ☩.
176		Æ ·9		
			Inscr. King, head and body radiate, half reclining, facing, on throne.	Similar.
177		Æ 1·		
178		Æ 1·		
179		Æ 1·		(inscr. retrograde). [Pl. xxix. 5.]
180		Æ ·9		[I. O. C.]
181		Æ ·9		,,
			Inscr. King, with head and body nimbate, seated cross-legged, facing, on cushions ; in l. hand, sceptre.	**MIOPO** Sun-god l., radiate ; r. hand advanced ; with l. grasps sword ; to l., ☩.
182		Æ 1·		[I. O. C.]
183		Æ 1·		
184		Æ ·8	(king not nimbate).	(deity holds wreath in r.). [Pl. xxix. 6.]
185		Æ ·95		
			Inscr. King, with body radiate, half reclining, facing on throne, flames on shoulders.	Similar.
186		Æ 1·1		(deity holds sceptre, not sword).
187		Æ 1·		
188		Æ 1·		(inscr. **MIIOPO**).
189		Æ ·85		
190		Æ ·85		(deity holds wreath in r.).

No.	Wt.	Metal. Size.	Obverse.	Reverse.
			PAONANOPAO OOHPKEKOPANO King, with head nimbate and body radiate, seated facing, head r., cross-legged on cushions; holds in l. hand, sceptre.	**NANA** Nanaia r., nimbate; holds sceptre; to r., � .
191		Æ 1·05		[I. O. C.]
			Similar.	**OKPO** Siva facing, nimbate, head l. ; has four arms and hands, in which he holds a wreath, a thunderbolt, a trident and a vase ; to l., ☷ .
192		Æ 1·05		
193		Æ ·9		
			Inscr. King, with head and body radiate, half reclining, facing, on throne.	Similar.
194		Æ 1·		[I. O. C. Pl. xxix. 7.]
195		Æ 1·		
196		Æ 1·		(Siva holds goat in fourth hand).
197		Æ ·9		(Siva grasps sword in fourth hand).

No.	Wt.	Metal. Size.	Obverse.	Reverse.

BAZODEO (VASU DEVA).

(a) *Gold.*

No.	Wt.	Metal. Size.	Obverse.	Reverse.
			PAONANO PAO BA ZOAHOKOPANO The king l., clad in conical helmet and suit of mail, diad. and nimbate ; holds r. hand over altar; in l., spear; wears sword.	**NANA** Nanaia r., nimbate, head surmounted by crescent; holds sceptre, ending in forepart of horse, and patera; to r , ⛫ .
1	122·5	*N* ·85		[Pl. xxix. 8.]
2	122·2	*N* ·8		[I. O. C.]
			PAONANOPA OBAZOΔHOK Similar.	**OKPO** Siva facing, having three faces and two arms ; holds wreath and trident; to l., ⛫ .
3	120·8	*N* ·8		
4	122·3	*N* ·8		(inscr. **OPKO**). [Pl. xxix. 9.]
			PAONANOPAOBA ZOAHOKOPANO The king l., clad in conical helmet and suit of mail, diad. and nimbate; holds r. hand over altar ; in l., spear; standard behind head.	**OKPO** Siva facing, having three faces and two arms ; holds wreath and trident; behind him, bull l. ; to r., ⛫ .
5	123·8	*N* ·8		[Pl. xxix. 10.]
6	124·9	*N* ·8		
7	123·5	*N* ·85		(Siva one-faced). [I. O. C.]
8	124·8	*N* ·85		(bull feeding).
9	123·4	*N* ·8		,, (inscr. **OPKO**). ,,
10	122·8	*N* ·85	(inscr. barbarous).	(Siva one-faced) ; symbol to l.

No.	Wt.	Metal. Size.	Obverse.	Reverse.
			PAONANOPAOBA ZOAΗOKOPANO The king standing as before at altar; beside which, trident fixed in the ground.	**OKPO** Siva, one-headed, facing; holds wreath and trident; behind him, bull l.; to l., 𝕏 .
11	126·	N ·85		
12	124·7	N ·85		
13	121·2	N ·8		
14	123·	N ·9	to r., (ꙮ) .	(inscr. **OqꙘO** ; to l., 𝕏).
15	124·	N ·85	,, ꙅ .	,, ,,
16	116·4	N ·85	,, ,,	,, ,,
17	31·	N ·5		,, ,, [I. O. C. Pl. xxix. 11.]
18	30·7	N ·5		(Siva crosses his legs) ; to r., 𝕏 .

Barbarous imitations.

No.	Wt.	Metal. Size.	Obverse.	Reverse.
19	122·7	N ·9	to r., (ꙮ) .	[Pl. xxix. 12.]
20	122·5	N ·9	,, ,,	to l., ⌐⌐ .
21	123·7	N 1·	,, ,, ; below, 卍 .	
22	125·5	N 1·05	,, ,, ,, ,,	
23	120·8	N ·95	,, ,,	to l., 卍 .
24	124·7	N 1·05	,, ,, ,, ,,	[Pl. xxix. 13.]

No.	Wt.	Metal. Size.	Obverse.	Reverse.
				(β) *Bronze.*
			PAONANOPAO BAZOAHOKOPANO * The king, standing as before, at altar; beside which, trident fixed in the ground.	OKPO Siva, one-headed, facing; holds wreath and trident; behind him, bull l.; to r., 𝍌.
25		Æ ·9		
26		Æ ·9	to r., 𝍌.	
27		Æ ·95	,, ,,	[Pl. xxix. 14.]
28		Æ 1·		
29		Æ ·85		
30		Æ ·95	(inscr. barbarous).	
31		Æ ·95	,, ,,	
32		Æ 1·	(trident absent).	(inscr. wanting). [I. O. C.]
			PAOBA ZOΔHO King, standing as above, at altar.	Similar (?).
33		Æ ·75		

* These legends are not complete on any specimen.

Y

No.	Wt.	Metal. Size.	Obverse.	Reverse.
			INDO-SCYTHIC, UNCERTAIN.	
			(a) *Gold ; without figure of King.*	
			Indian legend (see plate xxix. 15 ; the inscription seems to run on one side . . . . . *dideva-ta ?*). Greek city-goddess, clad in chiton and peplos, wearing mural crown, and holding a poppy-head.	**TAYPOC** Humped bull r. ん↑ヰ (*vrishabha*).
1	66·7	*N* ·6		[Pl. xxix. 15.]

SUPPLEMENT.

IMPORTANT TYPES NOT IN THE BRITISH MUSEUM.*

No.	Obverse.	Reverse.
	DEMETRIUS.	
1	Bust of the king r., diad.	**ΒΑΣΙΛΕΩΣ** Pallas facing, **ΔΗΜΗΤΡΙΟΥ** armed; holds lance and shield.
	[Pl. xxx. 1.]	Æ Wt. 243· (Gen. Cunningham): an injured specimen (Wt. 219·3), recently acquired for Brit. Museum.
2	Head of the king r., in elephant's skin.	Same inscr. Pallas seated l, holding spear in r., and shield in l.
	[Pl. xxx. 2.]	Æ round, ·7 (Gen. Cunningham).
3	**ΒΑΣΙΛΕΩΣ ΑΝΙΚΗΤΟΥ ΔΗ-ΜΗΤΡΙΟΥ** Bust of the king r., in elephant's skin.	𐨤𐨿𐨪𐨗 ... ... (*Māharajasa aparajitasa Deme* .....). Winged thunderbolt.
	[Pl. xxx. 3.]	Æ square, ·75 (Gen. Cunningham).

* In this list will be found the more important coins of the Greek and Scythic Kings which have been published, but are not represented in the British Museum. Mere varieties are not given, nor, in most cases, merely different denominations of already mentioned coins, unless when such denominations are higher than those of the British Museum Coins. To this Supplement belong three plates, the figures in which are in most cases due to Gen. Cunningham's valuable papers in the *Numismatic Chronicle*, and are reproduced by his kind permission. In one or two instances coins have been inserted here which were acquired for the British Museum too late for them to figure in their proper places.

No.	Obverse.	Reverse.

PANTALEON.

1 — Head of the king r , diad.

[Pl. xxx. 4.]

ΒΑΣΙΛΕΩΣ Zeus seated **ΓΑΝΤΑΛΕΟΝΤΟΣ** l. ; holds in l., sceptre, in r., a figure of the three-headed Hekate.

Æ Wt. 232· (Gen. Cunningham).

AGATHOCLES.

With name and type of Antiochus Nicator.

1 — **ΑΝΤΙΟΧΟΥ** Head of Antiochus **ΝΙΚΑΤΟΡΟΣ** I. r., diad.

[Pl. xxx. 5.]

ΒΑΣΙΛΕΥΟΝΤΟΣ Zeus striding **ΑΓΑΘΟΚΛΕΟΥΣ** to l., hurl- **ΔΙΚΑΙΟΥ** ing thunderbolt ; eagle at his feet : to l., wreath.

Æ Wt. 255· (Gen. Cunningham).

ANTIMACHUS I.

With name and type of Diodotus.

1 — **ΔΙΟΔΟΤΟΥ** Head of Diodotus **ΣΩΤΗΡΟΣ** r., diad.

[Pl. xxx. 6.]

ΒΑΣΙΛΕΥΟΝΤΟΣ Zeus striding **ΑΝΤΙΜΑΧΟΥ** to l., hurl- **ΘΕΟΥ** ing thunderbolt ; eagle at his feet : to l., wreath.

Æ Tetradrachm (The late Sir E. C. Bayley).

With his own types.

2 — Indian elephant r.

[Pl. xxx. 7.]

ΒΑΣΙΛΕΩΣ ΘΕΟΥ Nike l., **ΑΝΤΙΜΑΧΟΥ** holding wreath and palm, standing on prow of ship.

Æ round, ·9 (formerly Gen. Cunningham).

No.	Obverse.	Reverse.
	EUCRATIDES.	
1	Bust of the king r., helmeted.	ΒΑΣΙΛΕΩΣ ΜΕΓΑΛΟΥ The ΕΥΚΡΑΤΙΔΟΥ Dioscuri charging r., carrying palms.
	[*Rev. Numism.*, 1867, Pl. XII.]	N Wt. 2593·5 gr. (20 stater piece, Bibl. Nationale, Paris).
2		N Stater (Col. Strutt).
3	Bust of the king l., helmeted, but with shoulders bare; thrusting with spear.	As last.
	[Pl. xxx. 8.]	Æ Wt. 233· (Gen. Cunningham).
4	ΒΑΣΙΛΕΩΣ ΜΕΓΑΛΟΥ Bust ΕΥΚΡΑΤΙΔΟΥ of the king r., helmeted.	𐨀𐨤𐨌 (*Maharajasa mahatakasa Evukratidasa*). The Dioscuri standing side by side; hold spears and swords.
	[Pl. xxx. 9.]	Æ Wt. 34·5 gr. (formerly Gen. Abbott). On a coin of this class in Gen. Court's Collection, the inscription begins 𐨤𐨌 (Von Sallet in *Zeit. f. Num.* 10, p. 157).
5	Head of Apollo r., laur.	ΒΑΣΙΛΕΩΣ Horse l., standing. ΕΥΚΡΑΤΙΔΟΥ
	[Pl. xxx. 10.]	Æ round, ·7 (Vienna).
6	ΒΑΣΙΛΕΩΣ ΜΕΓΑΛΟΥ Bust ΕΥΚΡΑΤΙΔΟΥ of the king r., diad.	Indian inscr. as above. The pilei of the Dioscuri, surmounted by stars, and two palms.
	[Pl. xxx. 11.]	Æ square, ·55 (Gen. Cunningham).

No.	Obverse.	Reverse.
7	ΒΑΣΙΛΕΩΣ ΜΕΓΑΛΟΥ ΕΥ- ΚΡΑΤΙΔΟΥ Bust of the king r., diad. and helmeted. [Pl. xxx. 12.]	ᒋᐣᐪᕐᕁᐪᐣ ᒋᐪᐣ.∿.ᕰ ᒋᐣᕁᐪᕐᒋᕁ (*Māhārajasa rajadirajasa Evukratidasa*). Nike l.; holds wreath and palm. Æ square, ·7 (Gen. Cunningham).

HELIOCLES.

No.	Obverse.	Reverse.
1	Bust of the king r., helmeted.	ΒΑΣΙΛΕΩΣ Zeus seated l.; ΗΛΙΟΚΛΕΟΥΣ holds Nike ΔΙΚΑΙΟΥ and long sceptre. Æ Tetradrachm (formerly Major Hay).
2	[Pl. xxxi. 1.]	Æ Drachm (The late Sir E. C. Bayley).

ANTIALCIDAS.

No.	Obverse.	Reverse.
1	ΒΑΣΙΛΕΩΣ ΝΙΚΗΦΟΡΟΥ ΑΝΤΙΑΛΚΙΔΟΥ Bust of the king r , diad.	ᒋᐣᕀᐠᕾ ᒋᐪᐣ∿ᕰ (*Maha- ᒋᐣᕼᐤᕾᕁᒑ rajasa jaya- dharasa Amtialikidasa*). Elephant walking r.; wreath in raised trunk. Æ square, ·75 (Major Landon: now presented to British Museum).

ANTIALCIDAS AND LYSIAS.

No.	Obverse.	Reverse.
1	ΒΑΣΙΛΕΩΣ ΑΝΙΚΗΤΟΥ ΛΥΣΙΟΥ Bust of bearded Herakles r.; club on shoulder. [Pl. xxxi. 2.]	Inscr. as last. The caps of the Dioscuri, and two palms. Æ square, ·7 (Bodleian Library).

No.	Obverse.	Reverse.

THEOPHILUS.

1	ΒΑΣΙΛΕΩΣ ΔΙΚΑΙΟΥ Bust ⊡ΕΟΦΙΛΟΥ of the king r., diad. [Pl. xxxi. 3.]	୮ᚼΨᛜ ୮ᛦᚾ∿ᘏ (*Mahara-jasa dhramikasa Theuphilasa*). Herakles, crowning himself; holds in l. hand, club and lion's skin. Æ Wt. 36· (Gen. Cunningham).
2	ΒΑΣΙΛΕΩΣ ΔΙΚΑΙΟΥ ΘΕΟ-ΦΙΛΟΥ Head of bearded Herakles r.; club on shoulder. [Pl. xxxi. 4.]	୮ᛗᚾᛘ ୮ᚼΨᛜ ୮ᛦᚾ.∿ᘏ (*Māhārajasa dhramikasa Theuphilasa*). Cornucopiae. Æ square, ·8 (Gen. Cunningham).

ARCHEBIUS.

1	ΒΑΣΙΛΕΩΣ ΔΙΚΑΙΟΥ ΝΙΚΗ-ΦΟΡΟΥ ΑΡΧΕΒΙΟΥ Bust of Zeus r., diad.; sceptre on shoulder. [Pl. xxxi. 5.]	୮ᛜᛚᛝ ୮ᚼΨᛜ ୮ᛦᚾ.∿ᘏ ୮ᛚᛙᛞᛘ (*Māhārajasa dhramikasa jayadharasa Arkhebiyasa*). The caps of the Dioscuri, and two palms. Æ square, ·9 (Gen. Cunningham).

APOLLODOTUS.

1	ΒΑΣΙΛΕΩΣ ΣΩΤΗΡΟΣ [ΑΠΟΛΛΟΔΟΤΟΥ] Apollo seated r. on throne, holding out bow.	୮ᛜᛗᛞᛘ ୮ᛦᛚᛞ ୮ᛦᚾ∿ᘏ (*Maharajasa tradatasa Apaladatasa*). Tripod. Æ square, ·8 (Gen. Cunningham).

No.	Obverse.	Reverse.

STRATO I.

1 | ΒΑΣΙΛΕΩΣ ΕΠΙΦΑΝΟΥΣ ΣΩΤΗΡΟΣ ΣΤΡΑΤΩΝΟΣ Bust of the king r., diad.

[Pl. xxxi. 6.]

ᛒᚾᚾᛕ ᛕᚤᚷᛌ ᛕᚤᛌ.~ᛘ ᛕᚾᛉ (*Māhārajasa pratichhasa tradatasa Stratasa*). Pallas l.; holding aegis and hurling thunderbolt.

Æ Wt. 134· (Gen. Cunningham).

STRATO II.

1 | ΒΑΣΙΛΕΩΣ ΣΩΤΗΡΟΣ ΣΤΡΑΤΩΝΟΣ ΥΙΟΥ ΣΤΡΑΤΩΝΟΣ Bust of the king r., diad.

[Pl. xxxi. 7.]

ᛕᚾᛉ ᛕᛘᚾᛉᚾ ᛘᛉ~ᛠ ᛕᚾᛉ ᚾᛃᛝᛨᛞᛓ ᛃ ᛕᛌᚻ (*Maharaja rajarajasa Stratasa putrasa cha sampriyapita Stratasa*). Pallas l.; holding aegis and thunderbolt.

Æ Wt. 36· (Gen. Cunningham).

This is Gen. Cunningham's reading of his specimen (engraved), and given on his authority.

MENANDER.

1 | ΒΑΣΙΛΕΩΣ ΣΩΤΗΡΟΣ ΜΕΝΑΝΔΡΟΥ Head of Pallas r., helmeted.

[Pl. xxxi. 8.]

ᛕ.ᛌᛓᛉ ᛕᚾᛉᛘ ᛕᛝᛘ~ᛨ (*Māharajasa tradatasa Menadrāsa*). Owl r.

Æ Wt. 28· (Gen. Cunningham).

2 | ΒΑΣΙΛΕΩΣ ΣΩΤΗΡΟΣ ΜΕΝΑΝΔΡΟΥ Bust of the king l., wearing aegis and thrusting with spear.

ᛕᚾᚾᛕ ᛕᛝᛉ.~ᛨ ᛕ.ᛌᛓᛉ (*Māhārajasa tradatasa Menadrāsa*). Pallas l.; holding thunderbolt and aegis.

Æ Didrachm (Published by Gen. Cunningham from a sealing-wax impression).

No.	Obverse.	Reverse.
3	ΒΑΣΙΛΕΩΣ ΣΩΤΗΡΟΣ ΜΕΝΑΝΔΡΟΥ Young male head r., wearing wreath. [Pl. xxxi. 9.]	𐨤.𐨫𐨿𐨭𐨂 𐨤𐨪𐨿𐨜𐨿𐨫 𐨤𐨗𐨱.~𐨩 (*Māhārajasa tradatasa Menadrāsa*). Dolphin r. Æ square, 1·
4	Same inscr. Two-humped camel l. [Pl. xxxi. 10.]	Same inscr. Bull's head, facing. Æ square, 1· (Museum As. Soc. Bengal).
5	Same inscr. Elephant l. [Pl. xxxi. 11.]	Same inscr. Elephant-goad. Æ square, ·9 (Gen. Cunningham).
6	Same inscr. Boar's head r. [Pl. xxxi. 12.]	Same inscr. Palm-branch. Æ square, ·8

Nos. 3 and 6 are said by Gen. Cunningham to be in the East India Museum. This is incorrect, as the coins of this Museum are now in the British Museum, and these types are wanting.

EPANDER.

No.	Obverse.	Reverse.
1	ΒΑΣΙΛΕΩΣ ΝΙΚΗΦΟΡΟΥ ΕΠΑΝΔΡΟΥ Bust of the king r., diad. [Pl. xxxi. 13.]	𐨤𐨪𐨸𐨫𐨩 [𐨤𐨗𐨩~𐨱 (*Maharajasa*] 𐨤𐨫𐨱𐨪 *rajasa] jayadharasa Epadrasa*). Pallas l. ; holds aegis and thunderbolt. Æ Wt. 19· (broken), (Gen. Cunningham).

DIONYSIUS.

No.	Obverse.	Reverse.
1	Apollo r., clad in chlamys ; holds arrow with both hands. [Pl. xxxi. 14.]	𐨤𐨣𐨹𐨿𐨮𐨿𐨩𐨸 𐨤𐨪𐨿𐨜𐨿𐨫 𐨤𐨗𐨩~𐨱 (*Maharajasa tradatasa Dianisiyasa*). Royal diadema. Æ square, ·6 (Col. Bush).

z

No.	Obverse.	Reverse.

ZOILUS.

1	ΒΑΣΙΛΕΩΣ ΔΙΚΑΙΟΥ Bust ΙΩΙΛΟΥ of the king r., diad. [Pl. xxxii. 1.]	(*Māhā-rajasa dhramikasa Jhoilasa*). Herakles, facing; holds in r., wreath; in l., club and lion's skin; on his shoulder, Nike holding wreath. Æ Wt. 36·5 (Gen. Cunningham).
2	ΒΑΣΙΛΕΩΣ ΔΙΚΑΙΟΥ Head ΙΩΙΛΟΥ of bearded Herakles r., in lion's skin. [Pl. xxxii. 2.]	(*Maharajasa dhramikasa Jhoilasa*). Club and bow-case, within ivy-wreath. Æ square, 1·1 (Lady Headfort).

ARTEMIDORUS.

1	ΒΑΣΙΛΕΩΣ ΑΝΙΚΗΤΟΥ ΑΡΤΕΜΙΔΩΡΟΥ Bust of the king r., diad. [Pl. xxxii. 3.]	(*Māhārajasa apadihatasa Artemidorasa*). Artemis, clad in short chiton and chlamys, shooting l. Æ Wt. 128· (Gen. Cunningham). A specimen much injured (Wt. 117·3), recently acquired for British Museum.
2	(king helmeted). [Pl. xxxii. 4.]	Æ Wt. 36· (Gen. Cunningham).
3	Same inscr. Bust of the king r., diad. [Pl. xxxii. 5.]	Same inscr. Nike r.; holds wreath and palm. Æ Wt. 37· (Gen. Cunningham).

No.	Obverse.	Reverse.

PHILOXENUS.

1   The British Museum has recently acquired a didrachm (Wt. 140·) of this king with the usual type and inscriptions (p. 56), but having on the obverse a helmeted bust of the king l., thrusting with spear.

NICIAS.

1   ΒΑΣΙΛΕΩΣ ΣΩΤΗΡΟΣ **ΝΙΚΙΟΥ** Bust of the king r., diad.

[Pl. xxxii. 6.]

ꓱꓶꓶꓼ ꓱꓬꓶ.ᴪꓬ (*Mahā-* ꓱꓼꓩꟻ *rajasa tradatasa Nikiasa*). The king (or Pallas?) helmeted, standing l.; holds palm over shoulder.

Æ Wt. 36· (Gen. Cunningham).

TELEPHUS.

1   ΒΑΣΙΛΕΩΣ ΕΥΕΡΓΕΤΟΥ **ΤΗΛΕΦΟΥ** Giant (Skythes?), his body ending in three serpents; holds in each hand, hammer?

[Pl. xxxii. 7.]

ꓱꓴꓵꓢꟼꓶꓩ ꓱꓬꓶᴖꓴ ꓱꓩꟻꓵꓬ (*Maharajasa palanakramasa Teliphasa*). Helios radiate facing, clad in tunic and chlamys, holds long sceptre; beside him male figure wrapped in mantle, wearing wreath or horned: in field, mon.

Æ Wt. 37· (Bodleian Library).

Mr. Oman having kindly procured a cast of this coin, we are enabled to give a more accurate description of it than has hitherto appeared. Mr. Bendall suggests the reading *pālanakshamasa* as a rendering of εὐεργέτου.

AMYNTAS.

1   Gen. Cunningham possesses hemidrachms with the usual type of reverse, the seated Zeus; but having on the obverse respectively, (1) bust of the king in Macedonian causia; (2) bust of the king, bare-headed, thrusting with spear.

No.	Obverse.	Reverse.

HERMAEUS.

1 | Gen. Cunningham has a didrachm of the usual type (Wt. 153 grs.), with helmeted head of the king on the obverse.

2 | **ΒΑΣΙΛΕΩΣ ΣΩΤΗΡΟΣ ΕΡΜΑΙΟΥ** King on horseback r., galloping. | ౼౼౼౼ ౼౼౼౼ (*Maharajasa mahatasa Heramayasa*). Zeus seated l. on throne.

Æ Wt. 31· (Gen. Cunningham).

3 | **ΒΑΣΙΛΕΩΣ ΣΤΗΡΟΣ ΣΥ ΕΡΜΑΙΟΥ** Bust of the king r., bare.

[Pl. xxxii. 8.] | ౼౼౼[?౼౼౼౼౼] ౼౼౼ (*Maharajasa rajarajasa?] mahatasa Heramayasa*). Nike l. ; holding wreath.

Æ round, ·7 (Gen. Cunningham).

4 | ౼౼........ ౼౼ ౼౼౼.~౼ (*Māhārajasa raja .... [Herama?]yasa*). Horse r. | Uncertain device, surrounded by a circle of unascertained Chinese characters.

Æ 1· (Sir D. Forsyth), *Num. Chron.*, 1879, p. 276.

MAUES.

1 | **ΒΑΣΙΛΕΩΣ ΒΑΣΙΛΕΩΝ ΜΕΓΑΛΟΥ ΜΑΥΟΥ** Biga r., in which radiate figure holding sceptre or spear, and charioteer. | ౼౼౼౼ ౼౼౼౼౼ (*Rajadirajasa mahatasa Moasa*). Zeus seated l. on throne ; thunderbolt in extended r. hand.

Æ Didrachm (Bodleian Library), Wt. 121·

2 | | Æ Hemidrachm (acquired for Brit. Mus.), Wt. 27·6.

No.	Obverse.	Reverse.

AZES AND AZILISES.

1 | ΒΑΣΙΛΕΩΣ ΒΑΣΙΛΕΩΝ ΜΕΓΑΛΟΥ ΑΖΟΥ The king r., on horseback; lance couched.

𐨀𐨀𐨀 (*Maharajasa rajarajasa mahatasa Ayilishasa*). A city? l., holds in r. hand an object resembling a brazier; in l., palm bound with fillet.

[Pl. xxxii. 9.]

Æ Didrachm (R. Rochette, 1ᵉʳᵉ Suppl., Pl. II., No. 16).

2 | | Æ Hemidrachm (Grotefend).

AZILISES.

1 | 'Standing figure to the r., with the r. arm extended horizontally, and holding a chaplet.'

'Figure in short tunic, with loose veil-like garments around the head, &c. Arian legend, imperfect, ... *jasa mahatasa Ayilishasa.*'

Æ square (Thomas's Prinsep II., p. 212, No. 9, Sir E. C. Bayley).

VONONES AND SPALAHORES.

1 | 'ΒΑΣΙΛΕΩΣ ΒΑΣΙΛΕΩΝ ΜΕΓΑΛΟΥ ΟΝΩΝΟΥ Hercules, with club and lion's skin; r. hand raised to the head.'

'Arian legend: — *Spahora bhrata dhramikasa Spalahorasa.* Minerva to the l., armed with shield and spear; r. arm extended.'

Æ square (Thomas's Prinsep II., p. 204, No. 3, Mr. Brereton).

[*Ariana Antiqua*, Pl. viii. 9.]

No.	Obverse.	Reverse.

GONDOPHARES.

1	Bust of the king l., wearing Arsacid tiara, diad.	BAΓIΛΕШΓ BAΓIΛΕШN ΜΕΓΓ ΥΝΔοΦΕΡΗΓ ΑΥΤοΚΡΑΤο King seated r. on throne, holding sceptre; behind, Nike crowning him.
	[Pl. xxxii. 10.]	Æ Wt. 58· (Berlin, *Zeitschr. f. Num.* 1879, p. 358).

ZEIONISES.

1	Barbarous inscr. The king r., on horseback; arm extended.	Inscription ending ア7Ϟ.～ㅂ (*Ji-hāniasa*). The king facing; on one side, Nike; on the other, a wingless figure, crowning him.
	[Pl. xxxii. 11.]	Æ Didrachm (Thomas's Prinsep, Pl. xxviii. 5).

ARSACES DIKAIOS.

1	BAΓIΛΕΥΟΝΤΟΓ BAΓIΛΕ-ШΝ ΔIΚΑΙΟΥ ΑΡΓΑΚΟΥ The king, on horseback r.; r. hand raised.	Arian legend :—(*Māhārajasa raja-rajasa mahatasa Ashshakasa tra-datasa*). Type obliterated.* [On another specimen, Male figure to the left, holding a small figure in his right hand].
		Æ round (Cunningham).

* A coin of this class has a type thus described by Rollin and Feuardent, *Catalogue de Médailles*, No. 8296.—Figure militaire (?) diadémée debout, à g., tenant de la dr. une palme, la g. sur·son épée (?).

No.	Obverse.	Reverse.

ARSACES THEOS.

| 1 | BACIΛEWC ΘEOY .. CAKOY Horse r.

[Pl. xxxii. 12.] | Bow in case : fillet-border.

Æ square, ·7 (Berlin, *Zeitschr. f. Num.*, Pl. v. 2). |

KADPHISES II.

| 1 | BACIΛEYC OOHMO KAΔΦI-CHC King r., holding club ; seated in biga moving slowly to r.

[Pl. xxxii. 13.] | Usual reverse ; type, Siva standing (see p. 124).

N Stater (*Ariana Antiqua*, Pl. x. 9). |

KANERKES.

| 1 | PAONANOPAO K[ANHPKI] KOPANO Bust of the king r., helmeted, holding spear, above clouds. | HΛIOC Helios standing, radiate ; one hand advanced, the other grasping sword.

N Wt. 30·8 (Rollin and Feuardent). |

This coin, published by v. Sallet, is noteworthy as bilingual.

| 2 | PAO KA]NHPKI The king standing, at altar.

[Pl. xxxii. 14.] |]ΓOBOYΔO Buddha seated facing, cross-legged ; arms in posture of benediction.

Æ 1· (Berlin, *Zeitschr. f. Num.* 1879, Pl. ix. 1). |

INDEX 1.

TYPES.

Enclosure, Sacred.—Agathocles, 12.
Epander, Head of.—Epander, 169.
Eucratides, Head of. — Eucratides, 13 *sqq.*, 165 *sq.*
Euthydemus I., Head of.—Euthydemus, I., 4 *sq.*; Agathocles, 10.
Euthydemus II., Head of.—Euthydemus II., 8.

F.

Female figure, between stars.—Maues, 70.
Female figure : holds fillet.—Maues, 71 ; Azes, 89.
Fire-god.—Kanerkes, 130, 132 *sq.* ; Hooerkes, 136, 150 *sqq.*, 156.

G.

Giant.—Telephus, 171.
Goad, Elephant.—Menander, 169.
Gondophares, Head of. — Gondophares, 103 *sqq.*, 174.
Gorgon-head on aegis. (*See* Aegis.)

H.

Hecate in hand of Zeus. (*See* Zeus.)
Heliocles, Head of.—Heliocles, 21 *sqq.*, 166.
Heliocles and Laodice, Heads of.—Eucratides, 19.
Helios in quadriga.—Plato, 20.
Herakles, Young, standing.—Demetrius, 6 ; Euthydemus II., 8 ; Lysias, 29 *sq.* ; Zoilus, 52 ; Maues, 69 *sq.* ; Azes, 89 ; Azilises, 96 ; Spalahores with Vo-

nones, 98 ; Spalagadames with Vonones, 99 ; Uncert., 119 ; Hermaeus and Kadphises, 120 *sq.* ; Kadphises I., 122 ; Hooerkes, 138, 154 ; Theophilus, 167 ; Vonones and Spalahores, 173.
Herakles, seated. — Euthydemus I., 4 *sq.*; Agathocles, 10 ; Agathocleia and Strato, 43 ; Azilises, 95 ; Spalagadames with Spalyris, 100.
Herakles; Nike on shoulder.—Zoilus, 170.
Herakles, bearded, Head of —Euthydemus I., 5 ; Demetrius, 7 ; Euthydemus II., 8 ; Lysias, 29 ; Strato I., 42 ; Antialcidas and Lysias, 166 ; Theophilus, 167 ; Zoilus, 170.
Herakles, Young, Head of.—Agathocles, 10.
Heraüs, Head of.—Heraüs, 116.
Hermaeus, Head of.—Hermaeus, 62 *sqq.*, 172 ; Hermaeus and Kadphises, 120 *sq.* ; Kadphises I., 122.
Hermaeus and Calliope, Heads of.—Hermaeus and Calliope, 66.
Hermes, standing.—Maues, 71 ; Azes, 83 *sqq.*
Hippostratus, Head of. — Hippostratus, 59 *sq.*
Horse.—Euthydemus I., 5 ; Euthydemus II., 8 ; Heliocles, 22 ; Menander, 48 ; Hippostratus, 60 ; Hermaeus, 66, 172 ; Maues, 72 ; Azes, 89 ; Azilises, 96 ; Eucratides, 165 ; Arsaces Theos, 175.
Horse, Forepart of.—Hyrcodes, 118.
Hyrcodes, Head of.—Hyrcodes, 117 *sq.*

K

Kadaphes, Head of.—Kadaphes, 123.

Kadphises II., Head of.—Kadphises II., 126.

Kanerkes, Head of.—Kanerkes, 132.

King, standing.—Azilises, 96 ; Spalirises, 101 ; Spalirises with Azes, 102 ; Kadphises II., 126 *sq.* ; Kanerkes, 129 *sqq.*, 175 ; Bazodeo, 159 *sq.* ; Nicias, 171.

King, seated.—Maues, 71 ; Azes, 83 *sq.* ; Gondophares, 104 ; Sanabares, 113 ; Kadaphes, 123, Kadphises II., 124 *sqq.* ; Hooerkes, 138, 145 ; Hooerkes, 156.

King on horseback.—Antimachus II., 55 ; Philoxenus, 56, 171 ; Nicias, 58 ; Hippostratus, 59 *sq.* ; Hermaeus, 172 ; Hermaeus and Calliope, 66 ; Maues, 68 *sq.* ; Azes, 73 *sqq.*, 88 *sqq.* ; Azes and Azilises, 92, 173 ; Azilises, 93 *sqq.* ; Spalahores with Vonones, 98 ; Spalagadames with Vonones, 99 ; Spalagadames with Spalyris, 100 ; Spalirises, 100 ; Spalirises with Azes, 102 ; Gondophares, 103 *sqq.*; Abdagases, 107 *sq.*; Zeionises, 110 ; Uncert., 111 ; Soter, 114 *sqq.* ; Zeionises, 174 ; Arsaces Dikaios, 174.

King on elephant.—Hooerkes, 137 ; 153 *sq.*

King on camel.—Azes, 88.

King in biga.—Kadphises II., 175.

King crowned by Nike.—Gondophares, 174.

King on horseback, crowned by Nike.—Heraüs, 116.

King and City.—Zeionises, 110.

King between Nike and another.—Zeionises, 174.

King, half length.—Kadphises II., 124 ; Kanerkes, 132, 175 ; Hooerkes, 136 *sqq.*

King, Head of, helmeted.—Sophytes, 2 ; Eucratides, 14 *sqq.*, 165 ; Plato 20 ; Antialcidas, 26 ; Lysias, 29 ; Diomedes, 31 ; Archebius, 32 ; Strato I., 40 ; Agathocleia, 43 ; Menander, 44 *sq.* ; Apollophanes, 54 ; Philoxenus, 56 ; Amyntas, 61 ; Hermaeus, 63 ; Soter, 116 ; Kadphises II., 124 *sqq.* ; Kanerkes, 132 ; Hooerkes, 136 *sqq.* ; Heliocles, 166.

King, Head of, in causia.—Antimachus I., 12 ; Antialcidas, 25 *sq.* ; Amyntas, 171.

King, Head of, in elephant's skin.—Demetrius, 6, 163 ; Lysias, 29.

King, Head of, in tiara.—Sanabares, 113 ; Gondophares, 174.

King, Bust of, thrusting with spear.—Eucratides, 18, 165 ; Archebius, 32 ; Menander, 46 *sq.*, 168 ; Philoxenus, 171 ; Amyntas, 171.

L.

Lakshmī, beside lion.—Azes, 85.

Laodice, Head of. (*See* Heliocles and Laodice.)

Lion.—Azes, 85 *sqq* ; Azilises, 97 ; Zeionises, 111 ; Uncert., 111, 119.

Lion, Maneless.—Pantaleon, 9 ; Agathocles, 11 ; Menander, 50 ; Maues, 69.

Lysias, Head of.—Lysias, 29.

W.

War-god.—Kanerkes, 132 ; Hooer-kes, 138, 148.

Warrior, standing.—Arsaces Dikaios, 174.

Wheel.—Menander, 50.

Wind-god.—Kanerkes, 135.

Wreath and palm.—Antialcidas, 28 ; Antimachus II., 55.

Z.

Zeus, standing.—Heliocles, 21 *sqq.* ; Maues, 68 ; Azes, 73 *sqq.*, 83 ; Azes and Azilises, 92 ; Azilises, 93 ; Spalahores with Vonones, 98 ; Spalagadames with Vonones, 99 ; Spalirises, 100 ; Gondophares, 103, 106 ; Abdagases, 107 *sq.* ; Soter, 114, 116.

Zeus, thundering.—Diodotus I., 3 ; Agathocles, 10, 164 ; Antimachus I., 164 ; Archebius, 32.

Zeus, standing : holding Hecate.—Agathocles, 10.

Zeus, seated.—Agathocles, 10; Amyntas, 61, 171 ; Hermaeus, 62 *sqq.*, 172 ; Spalirises, 101 ; Heliocles, 166.

Zeus, seated, with Thunderbolt.—Maues, 70, 172.

Zeus, seated, and elephant.—Eucratides, 19 ; Antialcidas, 25 *sq.* ; Maues, 70.

Zeus, seated : holds Hecate.—Pantaleon, 164.

Zeus, Head of, diad.—Andragoras, 1 ; Archebius, 167.

Zeus, Head of, laur.—Diodotus I., 3 ; Euthydemus I., 5.

Zeus, Head of thundering.—Antialcidas, 27 *sq.*

Zoilus, Head of.—Zoilus, 52, 170.

INDEX II.

KINGS, TYRANTS, &c.

INDEX III.

TITLES OF KINGS.

A. GREEK.

ΑΔΕΛΦΙΔΕΩΣ Abdagases, 108.

ΑΔΕΛΦΟΥ ΤΟΥ ΒΑΣΙΛΕΩΣ Spalyris, 100.

ΑΝΙΚΗΤΟΥ Lysias, 29, 166 ; Artemidorus, 54, 170 ; Philoxenus, 56 ; Demetrius, 163.

ΑΥΤΟΚΡΑΤΟ[Gondophares, 174.

ΒΑΣΙΛΕΥΟΝΤΟΣ Agathocles, 10 ; Soter, 114.

ΒΑΣΙΛΕΥΟΝΤΟΣ ΒΑΣΙΛΕΩΝ Abdagases, 107 ; Arsaces Dikaios, 174.

ΒΑΣΙΛΕΩΣ ΑΔΕΛΦΟΥ Spalirises, 100.

ΒΑΣΙΛΕΩΣ ΒΑΣΙΛΕΩΝ Gondophares, 104 ; Kanerkes, 129.

ΒΑΣΙΛΕΩΣ ΒΑΣΙΛΕΩΝ ΜΕΓΑΛΟΥ Maues, 68, 172 ; Azes, 73, 173 ; Azilises, 92 ; Vonones, 98, 173 ; Spalirises, 101 ; Gondophares, 103, 174 ; Orthagnes, 109 ; Pacores, 110 ; Soter, 114 ; Kadphises II., 126.

ΒΑΣΙΛΕΩΣ ΜΕΓΑΛΟΥ Eucratides, 14, 165 ; Apollodotus II., 37 ; Hippostratus, 59 ; Azes, 90 ; Spalirises, 102 ; Gondophares, 105 ; Sanabares, 113.

ΔΙΚΑΙΟΥ Agathocles, 10, 164 ; Heliocles, 21, 166 ; Archebius, 32, 167 ; Strato I., 41 ; Menander, 50 ; Zoilus, 52, 170 ; Spalyris, 100 ; Theophilus, 167 ; Arsaces, 174.

ΕΠΙΦΑΝΟΥΣ Plato, 20 ; Strato I., 40, 168.

ΕΥΕΡΓΕΤΟΥ Telephus, 171.

ΘΕΟΤΡΟΠΟΥ Agathocleia, 43.

ΘΕΟΥ Euthydemus I., 10 ; Antimachus I., 12, 164 ; Gondophares, 103 ; Arsaces, 175.

ΝΙΚΑΤΟΡΟΣ Amyntas, 61 ; Antiochus of Syria, 164.

ΝΙΚΗΦΟΡΟΥ Antialcidas, 25, 166 ; Archebius, 32, 167 ; Epander, 51, 169 ; Antimachus II., 55.

ΣΑΚΑ ΚΟΙΡΑΝΟΥ (ΚΟΡΡΑΝΟΥ) Heraüs, 116.

ΣΑΤΡΑΠΟΥ Zeionises, 110.

ΣΩΤΗΡΟΣ Diodotus, 10, 164 ; Diomedes, 31 ; Apollodotus I., 34, 167 ; Apollodotus II., 37 ; Strato I., 40, 168 ; Menander, 44, 168 ; Dionysius, 51 ; Zoilus, 52 ; Apollophanes, 54 ; Nicias, 58, 171 ; Hippostratus, 59 ; Hermaeus, 62, 172 ; Ranjabala, 67 ; Gondophares, 105 ; Abdagases, 107 ; Soter, 114 ; Kadphises II., 126 ; Strato II., 168.

ΤΥΡΑΝΝΟΥΝΤΟΣ Heraüs, 116.

ΥΙΟΥ Zeionises, 111 ; Strato II., 168.

ΦΙΛΟΠΑΤΟΡΟΣ Apollodotus II., 37.

B. SCYTHIC, IN GREEK LETTERS.

ΖΑΟΟΥ Kadaphes, 123.

ΚΟΡΑΝΟ Kanerkes, 130 ; Hooerkes, 136.

ΡΑΟ Kanerkes, 130, 175 ; Hooerkes, 136.

ΡΑΟΝΑΝΟ Kanerkes, 130, 175 ; Hooerkes, 136.

ΣΥ Hermaeus, 120, 172 ; Kadaphes, 123.

ΧΟΡΑΝ (ΚΟΡΟΝ, &c.) Kadphises I., 122 ; Kadaphes, 123.

C. INDIAN TITLES AND WORDS.

Apadihatasa, Lysias, 29 ; Artemidorus, 54, 170 ; Philoxenus, 56.

Aparajitasa, Demetrius, 163.

Apratihatasa, Gondophares, 105.

Apratihatachakrasa, Ranjabala, 67.

Rajarajasa, Azes, 73, 173 ; Azilises, 94, 173 ; Gondophares, 104 ; Strato II.,
    168 ; Arsaces Dikaios, 174.
Rajine, Pantaleon, 9 ; Agathocles, 11.

Sachhadhramaṭhidasa, Kadaphes, 123.
Sagaba, Orthagnes, 109.
Sampriyapita, Strato II., 168.
Sarvaloga iṣvarasa, Kadphises II., 124.
Sasasa, Gondophares, 106.
Strategasa, Aspavarma, 91.

Tradatasa, Diomedes, 31 ; Apollodotus I., 34, 167 ; Strato I., 40, 168 ;
    Strato II., 37 ; Menander, 44, 168 ; Dionysius, 51, 169 ; Zoilus, 52 ;
    Apollophanes, 54 ; Nicias, 58, 171 ; Hippostratus, 59 ; Hermaeus, 62 ;
    Gondophares, 103 ; Abdagases, 107 ; Soter, 114 ; Kadphises II., 124 ;
    Arsaces Dikaios, 174.

Vrishabha, Uncert., 162.

Yavugasa (Yauasa), Kadphises I., 120 ; Kadaphes, 123.

INDEX IV.

REMARKABLE INSCRIPTIONS AND LEGENDS.

TABLE

FOR

CONVERTING ENGLISH INCHES INTO MILLIMÈTRES

AND THE

MEASURES OF MIONNET'S SCALE.

TABLE

OF

THE RELATIVE WEIGHTS OF ENGLISH GRAINS AND FRENCH GRAMMES.

Grains.	Grammes.	Grains	Grammes.	Grains	Grammes.	Grains.	Grammes.
1	·064	41	2·656	81	5·248	121	7·840
2	·129	42	2·720	82	5·312	122	7·905
3	·194	43	2·785	83	5·378	123	7·970
4	·259	44	2·850	84	5·442	124	8·035
5	·324	45	2·915	85	5·508	125	8·100
6	·388	46	2·980	86	5 572	126	8·164
7	·453	47	3·045	87	5·637	127	8·229
8	·518	48	3·110	88	5·702	128	8·294
9	·583	49	3·175	89	5·767	129	8·359
10	·648	50	3·240	90	5·832	130	8·424
11	·712	51	3·304	91	5·896	131	8·488
12	·777	52	3·368	92	5·961	132	8·553
13	·842	53	3·434	93	6·026	133	8·618
14	·907	54	3·498	94	6·091	134	8·682
15	·972	55	3·564	95	6 156	135	8·747
16	1·036	56	3·628	96	6 220	136	8·812
17	1·101	57	3·693	97	6·285	137	8·877
18	1·166	58	3·758	98	6 350	138	8·942
19	1·231	59	3·823	99	6·415	139	9·007
20	1·296	60	3·888	100	6·480	140	9·072
21	1·360	61	3·952	101	6·544	141	9·136
22	1·425	62	4·017	102	6·609	142	9·200
23	1·490	63	4·082	103	6·674	143	9·265
24	1·555	64	4·146	104	6 739	144	9·330
25	1·620	65	4·211	105	6·804	145	9·395
26	1·684	66	4·276	106	6·868	146	9·460
27	1·749	67	4·341	107	6 933	147	9·525
28	1·814	68	4·406	108	6·998	148	9·590
29	1·879	69	4·471	109	7·063	149	9·655
30	1·944	70	4·536	110	7·128	150	9·720
31	2·008	71	4·600	111	7·192	151	9 784
32	2·073	72	4·665	112	7·257	152	9·848
33	2 138	73	4·729	113	7·322	153	9·914
34	2·202	74	4·794	114	7·387	154	9·978
35	2·267	75	4·859	115	7·452	155	10·044
36	2·332	76	4·924	116	7·516	156	10·108
37	2 397	77	4·989	117	7·581	157	10·173
38	2·462	78	5·054	118	7·646	158	10·238
39	2·527	79	5·119	119	7·711	159	10·303
40	2·592	80	5·184	120	7·776	160	10·368

TABLE

OF

THE RELATIVE WEIGHTS OF ENGLISH GRAINS AND FRENCH GRAMMES.

Grains.	Grammes.	Grains	Grammes.	Grains	Grammes.	Grains.	Grammes.
161	10·432	201	13·024	241	15·616	290	18·79
162	10·497	202	13·089	242	15·680	300	19·44
163	10·562	203	13·154	243	15·745	310	20·08
164	10·626	204	13·219	244	15·810	320	20·73
165	10·691	205	13·284	245	15·875	330	21·38
166	10·756	206	13·348	246	15·940	340	22·02
167	10·821	207	13·413	247	16·005	350	22·67
168	10·886	208	13·478	248	16·070	360	23·32
169	10·951	209	13·543	249	16·135	370	23·97
170	11·016	210	13·608	250	16·200	380	24·62
171	11·080	211	13·672	251	16·264	390	25·27
172	11·145	212	13·737	252	16·328	400	25·92
173	11·209	213	13·802	253	16·394	410	26·56
174	11·274	214	13·867	254	16·458	420	27·20
175	11·339	215	13·932	255	16·524	430	27·85
176	11·404	216	13·996	256	16·588	440	28·50
177	11·469	217	14·061	257	16·653	450	29·15
178	11·534	218	14·126	258	16·718	460	29·80
179	11·599	219	14·191	259	16·783	470	30·45
180	11·664	220	14·256	260	16·848	480	31·10
181	11·728	221	14·320	261	16·912	490	31·75
182	11·792	222	14·385	262	16·977	500	32·40
183	11·858	223	14·450	263	17·042	510	33·04
184	11·922	224	14·515	264	17·106	520	33·68
185	11·988	225	14·580	265	17·171	530	34·34
186	12·052	226	14·644	266	17·236	540	34·98
187	12·117	227	14·709	267	17·301	550	35·64
188	12·182	228	14·774	268	17·366	560	36·28
189	12·247	229	14·839	269	17·431	570	36·93
190	12·312	230	14·904	270	17·496	580	37·58
191	12·376	231	14·968	271	17·560	590	38·23
192	12·441	232	15·033	272	17·625	600	38·88
193	12·506	233	15·098	273	17·689	700	45·36
194	12·571	234	15·162	274	17·754	800	51·84
195	12·636	235	15·227	275	17·819	900	58·32
196	12·700	236	15·292	276	17·884	1000	64·80
197	12·765	237	15·357	277	17·949	2000	129·60
198	12·830	238	15·422	278	18·014	3000	194·40
199	12·895	239	15·487	279	18·079	4000	259·20
200	12·960	240	15·552	280	18·144	5000	324·00

PLATES

LIST OF PLATES.

Pl. I.

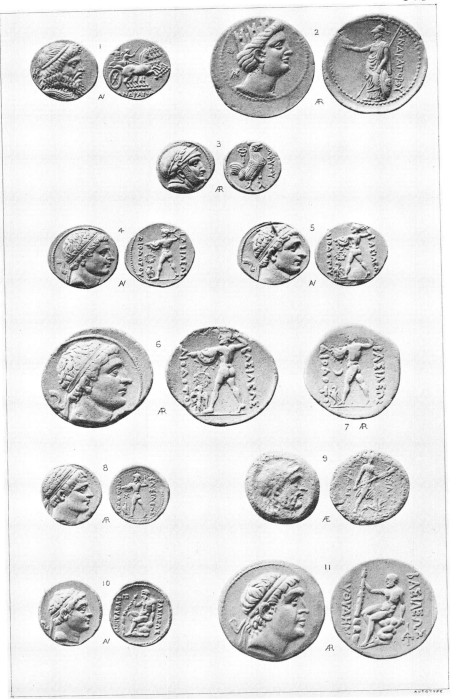

ANDRACORAS, SOPHYTES, DIODOTUS, EUTHYDEMUS I.

Pl. II.

EUTHYDEMUS I, DEMETRIUS.

Pl. III.

DEMETRIUS, EUTHYDEMUS II, PANTALEON.

Pl. IV.

ACATHOCLES.

Pl. V.

ANTIMACHUS I, EUCRATIDES.

Pl. VI.

EUCRATIDES, PLATO.

Pl. VII.

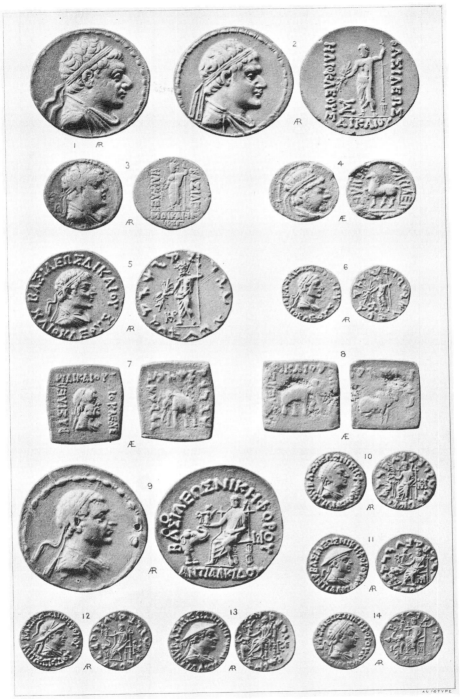

HELIOCLES, ANTIALCIDAS.

Pl. VIII.

ANTIALCIDAS, LYSIAS, DIOMEDES.

Pl. IX.

ARCHEBIUS, APOLLODOTUS.

Pl. X.

APOLLODOTUS, STRATO I.

Pl. XI.

STRATO I, AGATHOCLEIA, MENANDER.

Pl. XII.

MENANDER, EPANDER, DIONYSIUS, ZOILUS.

APOLLOPHANES, ARTEMIDORUS, ANTIMACHUS II,
PHILOXENUS, NICIAS.

Pl. XIV.

HIPPOSTRATUS, AMYNTAS.

Pl. XV.

HERMAEUS, CALLIOPE, RANJABALA.

Pl. XVI.

M·A·U·E·S.

Pl. XVII.

MAUES, AZES.

Pl XVIII.

AZES.

Pl. XIX.

AZES.

Pl. XX.

AZES, AZILISES.

Pl. XXI.

AZILISES, VONONES, SPALAHORES, &c.

Pl. XXII.

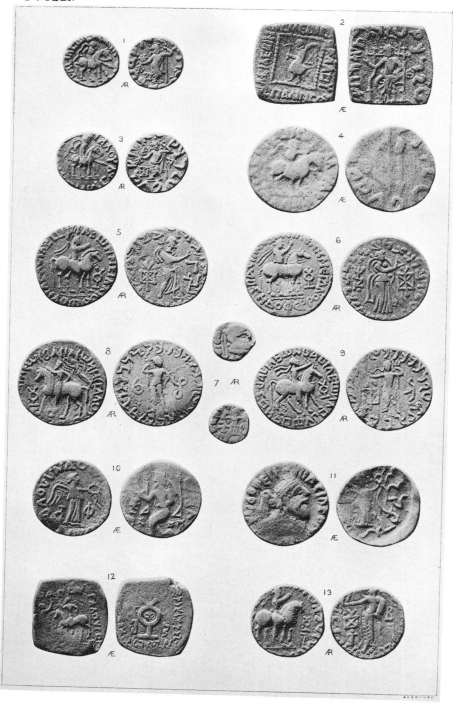

SPALIRISES &c. GONDOPHARES.

ABDAGASES, ZEIONISES &c. PACORES, ORTHAGNES,
SANABARES.

Pl. XXIV.

BAS. MEGAS, HERAUS, HYRCODES &c.

Pl. XXV.

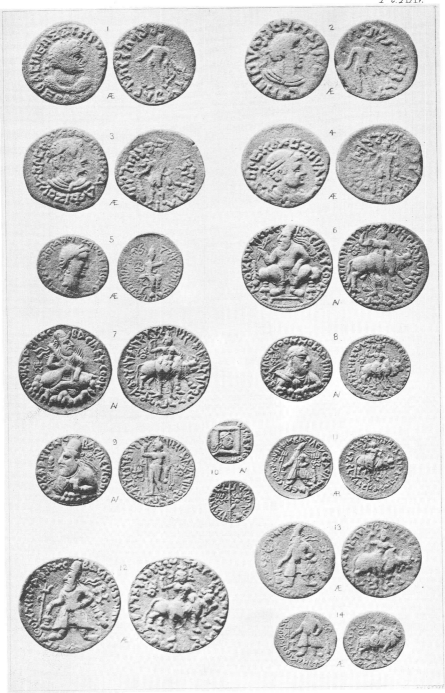

KADPHISES I, KADAPHES, KADPHISES II.

Pl. XXVI.

KANERKES.

Pl. XXVII.

KANERKES, HOOERKES.

Pl. XXVIII.

HOOERKES.

Pl. XXIX

HOOERKES, BAZODEO &c.

Pl. XXX.

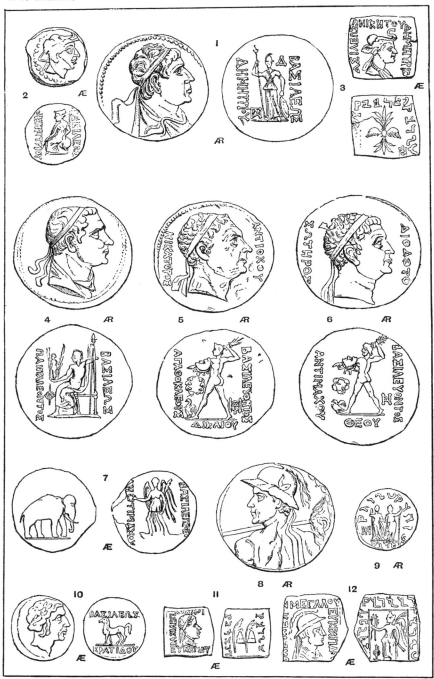

SUPPLEMENTARY. 1.

Pl. XXXI.

SUPPLEMENTARY. 2.

Pl. XXXII.

SUPPLEMENTARY. 3.